BUDDHA'S DOG
& OTHER MEDITATIONS

IRA SUKRUNGRUANG

Buddha's Dog

& Other Meditations

University of Tampa Press • Tampa, Florida

The University of Tampa Press
401 West Kennedy Boulevard
Tampa, FL 33606

ISBN 978-159732-156-3 (pbk.)
ISBN 978-159732-157-0 (hbk.)

Browse & order online at
www.ut.edu/TampaPress

Library of Congress Control Number: 2018932319

To Mick and Bonny,
Charlie and Ginger,
Keita,
and all the dogs of this world . . .

Contents

I

The Dog Without a Bark · 3
The Animatronic Dog · 6
Eat · 17
Yummy · 35
Sensitive Boy · 43
My Heart. Open. · 57
Noisy Neighbor · 70
My Dog Ginger · 85

II

On Trenton Doyle Hancock's Self-Portraits · 89

III

Thirteen Ways of Looking at Fat · 103
Fattest, Ugliest, Weirdest · 109
Secret · 120
The Uncovering · 123
Summer Days, 1983 · 131
Twitch, Blink, Shiver · 134

IV

A Sequence of Thoughts Without Any Kind of Order · 141
A Meditation on Pain · 152
Atlas, Don't Let Me Down · 165
Meditation on Monsters · 177

Acknowledgments · 186
About the Artists · 188
About the Author · 189
About the Book · 190

I

The Dog without a Bark

There was this dog, a Sheltie I believe, that had no voice. She was adopted, and her prior owners cut her vocal cords. This was the story around town. She lived across the street from my elementary school, and at three o'clock when the school bell rang, she ran along the fence and tried to bark at kids. I was eight or nine, old enough to walk home three blocks by myself. I had never met a dog without a bark. Some of the kids barked back. Some threw sticks at her, which sent her into a bigger silent frenzy. I watched and listened. Sometimes I was in such awe of her I stopped on the sidewalk for long seconds before moving on.

The dog without a bark would have been loud. She barked as if she knew she had nothing to offer, only rushes of rasped wind. I imagined if she did have a voice that bark would ring louder than any other dog in Chicago, any other dog in the world. Every day, at the same time, she was at it. Running and barking silence. And every day, the only thought that ran through my head was, *Where is your voice?*

Once, I stayed after to clean the chalkboard erasers. Everyone had made it home, and Austin Avenue was absent its schoolyard chatter. When I arrived at the corner, there she was, waiting and looking at the world through a rusty chain-link fence. At the sight of me she began bark-rasping. I took two steps and stopped. She took two steps and stopped. In my memory, she was a beautiful dog, white on the tip of her tail and ears and along her chest, the rest a light brown of milk chocolate.

I turned and looked at her. I said, "No one can hear you."

She didn't stop rasping.

I said, "I feel sorry for you."

She didn't stop.

"It must suck."

Rasp. Rasp. Rasp.

"Suck" was the new word I had learned. I was learning new words outside the vocabulary list daily and liked to use them whenever I could. I was learning a lot of other things, too: long division, the differences between the tundra and the deciduous forest, who ended slavery, and the quieter you were the less likely you would attract attention.

I found myself at the fence. I put my fingers through the chainlink, called to the dog in the voice I'd heard people do who had dogs—soft, soothing, solicitous.

I don't remember what I said, but the Sheltie came straight to me, smelled my fingers and licked. Her nose was wet. Her tongue too. Both made me giggle.

If my Thai mother had seen my interaction with the voiceless dog, she would've gone into shock. She would've told me how stupid I was. She would've told me about the dogs in Thailand, the ones that sunned in the dusty roads and howled wildly at the moon. All dogs were dangerous, she would've said, even ones without a voice, especially ones without a voice. But I felt like I had made my first real friend, and that friendship lasted a few minutes before I picked up my backpack and ran home.

ತನ

I couldn't kick the feeling that, perhaps, the dog and I had known each other once. It might be the only time reincarnation made sense to me. As a Buddhist, I had been raised to look forward to the next life. My mother taught me that we were living only for tomorrow. That one day would pass into another. Month to month. Year to year. Lifetime to lifetime. In each of these lives would be the same people in different roles, and maybe, as different species. In that moment, with that Sheltie, I felt that I had known this feeling before—this comfort, this connection that was like the long white string that wound around the praying hands of Buddhist monks.

I remember that Sheltie for the lessons I carry with me: you don't need a voice to know what you want. You don't need to sound like everyone else to make yourself heard.

The Animatronic Dog

Every summer from the ages of five to eight, my family drove from Chicago to Orlando to visit my mother's Thai nursing school friends, and every year, we stood in endless lines at Magic Kingdom, exhausted and claustrophobic at the sheer amount of people.

One attraction, however, never had a wait: The Carousel of Progress, a twenty-minute show that catalogs the technological advances of the twentieth century via an ageless American—white—family. It is full of the things I've come to despise: fake Americana music, the idea of the perfect nuclear family, and capitalist ideals. But then, young and clueless about just about everything, the Carousel of Progress gave my family and me a respite from the agonizing Florida heat.

In truth, the attraction wasn't all that bad. Hokey? Yes. Melodramatic? Definitely. What struck me was no matter what year it was—1900 or the future of 2000—this American family always had a dog, Rover. From one decade to the next, there he was, the classic American mutt, tongue sloppily slung to the side of his mouth, tail wagging like a metronome. He was obedient—sitting pretty, more attentive to his owner than we were.

I found myself fixated on Rover. I pointed and said, "mah," dog in Thai, until one of my parents told me to hush up. I sat between my parents—always between—and the warmth of their bodies comforted me. Rover was unlike the dog toys I possessed. He was not like Bobo, the black-eared stuffed animal, who had been watching over me since I was born. He was not like Pokey, the sprawling white mutt I used as a cushion when I watched cartoons about cartoon dogs. He was not Charlie, the battery-operated yapper, who promptly went still after three months. Rover seemed real to me the way real dogs were real. I wanted to pet his animatronic head, made out of synthetic hair. I wanted to snuggle against his animatronic side, feel the thrum of gears that made him work. I wanted to sniff his animatronic breath, which carried the scent of oil. Rover, even without life, even if programmed to do the same thing for decades, was an example of family stability, and family stability, though I did not know it then, was what mattered most.

A strange thought came to me: What if my mother and father could be on display, too, that we could be robots and last forever?

Here is my mother sporting a beehive hairdo and a pastel housedress, and my father in a pink golfing polo and brown slacks. Here is my mother sewing Thai dresses under the Buddha in our living room, and my father putting at a masking-tape X on the teal carpet. And here is me, their chubby son, glasses like petri dishes, sliding down the stairs in a laundry basket, and the glorious sound I would make, the shrill screech of happiness, the sudden rush of air that tousles my soft hair. We would travel reincarnated lifetimes: a Thai family in the Wild West, my mother driving the horses, my father with a holstered revolver to protect our livestock; a family in Siam before the fall of Sukhothai, my father standing strong against the Burmese, my mother crying for the safety of his life; a family witnessing the blessing of the real Gotama Buddha under the weighty branches of a Bodhi tree—we would be birds nested in the top branch.

In each lifetime, one thing remained consistent: we were always together.

What about the year 2000? What would our world look like then?

My mother alone in Chicago, looking out the window, dreaming of her return to Thailand. My father in Thailand, looking out the window, thinking of the roads he's been on, the wrong turns he has taken. And what of that boy, no longer a boy, at twenty-four, who thinks of his past constantly, even his other lives and the steps he has taken to get him to this one?

Amid all of this: where would Rover be? In which lap would he lay his robotic head?

ೞ

On an autumn day, the neighborhood dogs dashed back and forth, scattering fallen leaves in the wake of their run; or lounging on the front porch; or retrieving a ball. Dogs barked to one another, conversations across streets or through fences. There were so many dogs, my mother hated walking the suburban neighborhood, afraid that the tiny Yorkie from across the street would come charging and clamp on her ankles or the golden retriever would trample her small frame or the Jack Russell terrier would use her leg as a hydrant.

In my mother's stories, however, there was nothing for her to fear. In her stories, dogs were beloved, cared for, majestic animals. In her stories, dogs were loyal and obedient to the core. This I would learn about my mother: she was a woman who dwelled in polarity. Sometimes, when scolding me, she would say, "Be like dog. Stand by Mama all the time. OK?"

My favorite story involved Buddha and his dog. Buddha was my mother's version of Superman, a man without weakness who possessed many powers, and taming animals was one of them. He calmed the spiteful cobra. He pacified the heart of a rampaging bull. Birds fluttered around his head. Mice eased into the folds of his robes. My mother's stories stilled me before I drifted to sleep. It was the only way I could relax, let go of my day, and ease into slumber.

"Buddha," my mother would start, "once confronted a starving dog." He meditated in the thick of a forest, and a dog scampered around the brush, eying Buddha and the meals his disciples left for him. How could you blame a dog when there was the scent of meat in the air? This dog was ribcage-thin and haggard from days without eating or drinking.

"He looked like this," my mother would say and suck in her cheeks.

Buddha did not take notice of the dog at first. He was in his mind, and his mind was clear of thought, especially that of a lurking dog. When Buddha roused from his meditative state, he noticed the dog eating the last of his meal. He was not angry. He was not afraid. He was not even surprised. The dog just happened to be, like the trees and air and birds around him.

"Dog," Buddha said, "eat what is not offered; offer what is not eaten." Buddha moved toward the dog. The dog growled. Bared its teeth.

"Dog," Buddha said in a calming voice, "a hand is only a threat to the object it touches." Buddha reached out. The dog snapped the air, teeth clicking. This did not deter Buddha, who wore the same serene expression on his face, who did not flinch.

The dog did not want to give up his last morsel of food, which tasted divine and filled his empty belly and nourished his bones. This might be the last morsel he would have in his life—a short life, a life not explored—and so to protect himself, he lunged at Buddha.

Buddha raised his golden glowing hand. The glow touched the dog and went through him in waves of comforting heat, and the dog remembered being born again. He remembered his mother and the softness of her fur, remembered her wet nose that nuzzled him and her milk which she provided willingly. And the dog thought of his brothers and sisters heaped on top of each other and how he could feel their heartbeat in rhythm with his, that their breath was his breath. He remembered that he was not always hungry. That he was loved. That he was wanted. That he was not alone.

The dog ceased its attack. He bowed at Buddha's feet, whimpering.

"Dog," Buddha said, "you have traveled a hard road." He knelt down and patted the dog. The dog relished every moment of it, but did not ask for any more than he was to receive. The dog forgot that he was hungry, forgot he was lonely, forgot he was unloved, because now he was none of those things.

"Dog," Buddha said, "Let our paws travel in the same steps."

Together, Buddha and the dog lived out the rest of their days.

"The end," my mother would say, and sometimes, she added, "Live forever like us."

For a long time now, I've wondered where my mother learned this story. I've wondered whether she carried it with her when she came to America, whether it was a story told to her when she was a child, her mother touching her hair, caressing her cheek, as she drifted to sleep. She had the knack of storytelling, blessed with a vivid imagination, blessed with an animated voice. It was her stories of Buddha and his dog, however, that made me believe we weren't different, canine and human, that we craved the same thing, that loneliness was not a one-species phenomenon. That, perhaps, it wasn't only Buddha's enlightened mind that led him to Nirvana, but the companionship of a dog.

જી

Fridays were Show & Tell in Mrs. S's first grade class. I was never keen on Show & Tell, an hour-long segment of the day dedicated to showcasing cool toys my parents did not buy me.

Once I brought my stuffed animal, Bobo, and the other boys laughed. "Do you cuddle with that?" someone said. Already, these boys were posturing. It happened to all Chicago boys, born and bred in working-class families. They postured. They stuck out their chins and chests like their factory-worker fathers, learned to form their words in the gut. Secretly, I'm sure, they had their own stuffed animals like Bobo, their own blankies they clung to. They never brought them to Show & Tell—only G. I. Joes, only remote control cars, only whoopee cushions.

That day, my Show & Tell item was a Thai coin, one satung, and Tanya Tallon, one of the nicest girls in the school, did not bring the usual girl thing. What she brought was something that made the class silent, made Mrs. S who usually sat in a rocking chair off to the side take Tanya in her arms.

We sat on the classroom floor, Indian-style, and when it was Tanya's turn, she stood up, her hands linked behind her back. Tanya came from an enormous family and lived a block or two away from Harnew Elementary. Usually, she wasn't shy, but today, up in front of us, she did not meet our eyes but stared at the space between her feet.

"Tanya," Mrs. S said. "What did you bring today?" Mrs. S must have noticed Tanya's peculiar behavior because she straightened in the rocker. On a daily basis, Mrs. S handled crying. It was the job of a first-grade teacher, wasn't it? To sense the moment tears were about to spill. To teach us how to read and write and count. Usually cries stemmed from a fall or a fight. I assumed Mrs. S had become an expert cry detector, noticing quivering lips, held breaths of anger, change in color, balled-up hands. I was sure that afternoon she could sense a cry coming.

But Tanya did not cry. She extended her right arm. What lay in her hand looked like a watch.

"What is it, honey?" Mrs. S said.

"A collar," Tanya said, her voice aimed at the floor.

The collar was a faded red. It had a silver pendant on it, and I thought it was a Buddha, like the one I kept hidden around my neck.

"Tell us more," Mrs. S said.

"This collar was my dog's," Tanya said.

"It's pretty," Mrs. S said. "What's your dog's name?"

I don't remember the dog's name, but I remember Richie Hogren saying how the dog liked to bark at him through the fence. I remember him saying he was pretty. Richie lived across the street from Tanya and had a wild head of brown hair and deep, deep dimples. He and Tanya walked to school together. "I'm sorry, Tanya," Richie said.

"For what, Richie?" Mrs. S said.

"My dog died," said Tanya. "I loved him very much. I miss him."

"Sweetheart," said Mrs. S and her face softened. No longer did she look like a witch who threatened misbehaved kids with her evil eye. "Tell us what you miss most about him."

Tanya raised her eyes to the class for the first time. "He liked to roll around on his back."

"My dog does that," someone said.

"Mine too," said another.

Tanya smiled, a few teeth missing. "It's funny. He had such an itchy back."

"Would you like to pass the collar around?" Mrs. S said.

Tanya nodded and handed it to the person in front; it made a soft clink from person to person.

"What else do you remember?" Mrs. S said.

Tanya thought about it. She wore pink overalls that day and

white sneakers with pink laces. Her hair was tied up in a pink scrunchy. "At night, he slept with me. He could've slept with my sisters, but he slept with me. He was soft, especially behind the ears. I liked touching him there, and he liked it too."

"That's a good memory," Mrs. S said. "Your dog isn't truly gone if you remember that."

This was when the cry began. Not a loud cry. Not a heaving cry. It was silent, the first silent cry I had ever witnessed, the reason I remember this moment so well. It was a cry that did not express pain, but longing. I cried like this ten years later when my father moved out that winter day, and I knew I had lost something in my life—my sense of family.

The class did not know what to do, so we sat and watched. There was a lesson here, we all knew it, but how deeply we understood was another question. We were six after all; there was still so much for all of us to learn, beyond reading and writing, about the human heart and how much joy and pain it can hold.

Mrs. S rose from the rocking chair and scooped Tanya into her arms. She sat back down and rocked her. Tanya hid her face into Mrs. S's shoulder. "It's all right," Mrs. S kept repeating.

The collar made it to me. It was light in my hands, the texture rough on my skin. The dog tag jingled. I squeezed it, and did what my mother told me to do when speaking of the dead. I prayed to Buddha. I blessed the dog and wished him luck in his next journey, whatever that may be, wished what my mother always said to wish for when we passed road kill or when I accidentally stepped on an ant. I wished the animal to be born into a human life, and to be loved.

℘

When you grow up with dogs, you grow up with a sense of loss. You grow up knowing that your dogs have shorter lifespans, that your time with them is limited. You are prepared for what is inevitable.

My ex-wife and best friend, Katie, has grown up her entire life with dogs. Going through her family photos, I would be hard-pressed to find one that did not include dogs. The phases of Katie's life are measured out by their lives. They become pillars of memory, a way to access years. "This happened," she would say, "when Bonny was first a pup." For her, there has been a list of dogs. Sergeant, the German shepherd mix. Hawk, the husky. Amber, the cocker spaniel. Alex, the mutt with the softest ears, and then the golden retrievers, Andrew, Mick and Bonny. And then our dogs, Ginger, Charlie, and Savvy. Katie understands love and loss, understands it over and over again.

In Geoff Schmidt's expertly woven essay, "Otis & Jake," he describes the lives of his two dogs—one about to pass on and the other a rambunctious puppy—and juxtaposes them to the birth of his first child and the end of his marriage. At the end of the essay, Schmidt writes:

> "Why do we take things close to our hearts, why do we love? We know the dogs we take in as puppies will grow old, will get sick, will know pain, will die. We know that we will outlive them, that they will be seized by a kind of suffering that we can never lift…When you lose love it mauls your heart. It bloodies you. And yet, again and again, we choose to love. Again and again. Why do we choose to love, again and again and again?"

There is no logical answer, of course, except as Buddha says, we are born with love etched into our being. It is the reason we cling. It is the reason we cry. But as soon as we emerge into the world, as soon as we gulp our first breath of air, begins our first lesson of loss. The two are inexorably linked.

Not long after Tanya's Show & Tell, I asked my mother for a dog. I was trying to be less Thai and more American. Being Thai meant I got picked on at school. Meant I was different. I said so to my mother, who laughed at my request like it was the most absurd thing I uttered in my life.

"Crazy," she said in Thai. "A dog will bite your face off."

I told her lots of kids at school had dogs and not one had their face bitten off.

"Something always gets bitten," she said.

I told her she was loco, a word I learned from the only Hispanic in class.

"How about a doll dog?" my mother said.

Bobo, Pokey, Charlie—I tortured them with my love. My mother worked as a nurse, and often, she came home with brand-new syringes and surgical scissors. With my instruments at hand, I dissected my dog pals. I cut open their ears and gave them shots of water. I was saving them with my medical expertise. Giving them new life. Soon, they rotted from the inside and out came this moldy stench. Soon, my mother would tire of sewing on ears and paws and eyes and noses, and eventually they would find their way into the trash.

My father arrived home just then. I don't remember where he had been, probably the golf course or driving range. My mother told him about my request.

He pulled up his right pant leg and pointed to large indentations below his knees and on his calf. I had seen the scars before; I used to trace my fingers on them.

"You see?" my mother said.

"Crazy dog bit my leg," he said.

"Tell your son what dogs do," my mother said.

"They bite," said my father.

"Always," my mother said.

Admittedly, knowing the origins of my father's scars made me a bit apprehensive. And I truly believed my mother thought all dogs would bite faces. The other part of me, the young and dumb part of me, which was growing at an accelerated rate, thought having a scar might be cool. Scars were tough, and tough I wasn't. Having a dog might boost my image as a tough guy, and perhaps, if all dogs bite as my mother insisted, I could train my dog to bite the bullies at school. Imagine that. I could bring my dog—some demonic hellhound—to Harnew Elementary and he would sit by my desk, growling in a low rumble at every first grader who posed a threat. I could teach him a secret code word, like "poophead," my favorite word at the time, my favorite word now, and that would send my dog, who I think I would name He-Man, into a mandible-snapping rage. "He-Man," I would say. "Poophead."

My father cleared his throat. He always knew how to change the subject. "No dog. How about ice cream?"

Dog forgotten.

ఌ

But I'm thinking now, a dog could have saved us. A dog could've changed the course of our family life, and perhaps we would have loved each other more, perhaps a divorce was not inevitable. Perhaps a dog could've spared me from my mother's suffocating love. Perhaps a dog could've taught us about the tender parts of our hearts, about fragility, about sacrifice. And we would have looked to it as we looked to Buddha, for some sort of guidance, some sort of direction. In the end, American was not what we wanted to be, despite what we told ourselves. What we wanted was to be a family, like the one at the Carousel of Progress, the one that moved from decade to decade, lifetime to lifetime, whole and happy, Rover always near, barking and wagging.

Eat

The world became larger that year, 1979. No longer did it stop at the end of the driveway. No longer did I find myself in my neighbor's apple tree, gazing from the top, wondering what was over the fence and across the six-lane street. No longer did we speak one language in the house and another in public places. That summer, my family boarded a plane to Thailand—my mother's first return in over a decade—and the world expanded across an ocean, to another continent, to another country where heat sizzled roads and torrential rain chased cockroaches into corners.

My family traveled to Bangkok for more than a visit. We came to pay our respects to my grandfather, my mother's father, the man who dreamt of Buddha and raised a family of nine single-handedly. Grandfather Chua was in the hospital, lungs failing from too many years smoking a pipe, and now his withered body could not sustain itself.

None of this was explained to me. For the first few days, I sat outside on the cool marble deck and waited for my cousins Oil and Ant to come back from school. My mother was away with her sisters and brothers at the hospital, so I stayed with my father, who took childcare less seriously. He spent much of his time on the phone, talking to old friends, scheduling lunches and golf outings.

I was accustomed to entertaining myself. I was an only child with two working parents. Give me a piece of paper and pencil and I would draw anything. Even at three, I had the power to mimic. I wasn't the strongest artist, and I couldn't imagine something and draw it, but if my subject was stationary, I could get it somewhat right.

So I drew the dogs. Because I was instructed to never touch them—Thai dogs, according to my mother, were mean—this was the next best thing. I felt like I was learning something essential in my sloppy drawings that touching would never allow. I was doing what Buddha instructed: seeing beyond the physical.

એ

The housedogs had their own routines. I watched them. I drew them. Bobo was a tri-colored male, youth unbound, pouncing on random things at random times—a butterfly, a stick, one of the other dogs. Bobo adored my aunt Jeeb, forcing his broad head under her hand, and when she swept the driveway he playfully bit at the whisks of the broom. Anut was the female of the three, the matriarch. She strutted with an elegance the other two did not possess, and if she could speak, I imagined her with a proper English accent. Her bark was operatic with a repeated lilt at the end. And then there was Pokey the runt, a skinny, light-colored mutt, who was unsteady on his legs with a noticeable tremble. His nose was discolored, brown and pink, and his ears stood straight up. He had long whiskers like a cat, and patches of his fur were missing; underneath that fur was rashy skin. Pokey sounded like a dog who smoked—raspy, unintimidating. He found the coolest and shadiest places to lie down and had a way of watching you, his stare unflinching, as if he were studying your heart.

I fell for Pokey. We were alike, even though we were different species, even though he was thin and I was round. I was a boy drawn to odd things, discarded toys instead of brand new ones. Things lost and found held larger value to me because I created narratives for them; they allowed me to imagine their other lives before becoming mine. Later, I desired not the most beautiful girls, but the strangest. This attraction made me say Pokey's name often, made me sing it to the tune of "Happy Birthday," the only song I knew. He'd stare, tilt his head, wag his tail, and sometimes bark as if he were adding his own vocals.

The dogs went about their day, like me, without the need of anything but a shaded, cool place to lie down. They entertained themselves. Chased insects. Played with each other. Barked at every passerby—the mail person, the man who sold ice cream from a cart, the monks on their morning alms walk. Their barks became like hourly chimes of a clock, telling us how much time was left in the day.

There was one person the dogs could not live without. Aunt Jeeb was the center of their world. When she came home after teaching grade school, they squeaked and jumped on her with reckless joy. She brought home special treats, like grilled meatballs slathered in sweet chili sauce. The other sisters called her the dog whisperer. They called her crazy, too, for spoiling her puppies and taking in dogs that required the most care. Even at a young age, they said, Aunt Jeeb had the knack of understanding what a dog wanted. She spent much of her youth with dogs instead of people, cleaning their wounds, picking off ticks from their skin. It was not uncommon to see a line of strays following her to school like she was a prophet.

One day, when my mother and father were both away, Aunt Jeeb babysat me. My cousins were finishing off their homework in their rooms, and Aunt Jeeb and I sat on the marble deck with the dogs. Bobo, Anut, and Pokey gathered around her, curled into tight little balls. I drew them, and because she was there, I drew her too.

"Do you like dogs?" she said in Thai.

I nodded.

"Me too," she said. She smiled, and I drew it.

"Do you know why I love dogs?"

I shook my head.

"Because they love you no matter what." She patted Bobo with her feet. The tip of his tail swooshed the ground. "They need us."

I drew my aunt's hands, which were around a cup of tea. I drew the steam that rose from the cup. Her eyes traveled to a blossoming needle plant.

"Do you want to touch them?" she said.

I nodded. Dropped my pencil. Sat on my toes.

"Come," she said. She rose off the porch's ledge, and the dogs looked up at her. "Bobo," she said, "sit." Bobo sat, his tail sweeping the ground, his tongue sloppily slung to the side.

I heard my mother's voice in my head. Heard her warnings of touching a dog.

"It's OK," Aunt Jeeb said. "He won't bite."

Aunt Jeeb offered her hand to me. I took it because when she smiled like this she looked like my mother. She placed my hand on Bobo's right shoulder. My hand sank into him, felt his warmth, his sturdiness. I stood as tall as he was, his breath hot on my face.

"Anut," my aunt said, and Anut sat up and raised her elegant chin. I touched her at the same place and noticed her fur was softer than Bobo's, smooth like my mother's nightgown. Anut sniffed my forehead. Her wet nose touched my skin.

"Pokey," my aunt said, and Pokey did not rise. He lay flat on his side. "Be gentle. Pokey is old." My fingertips grazed him, his ribcage like hills under my fingers.

"Good," she said. "Pokey likes it."

Pokey kept his eyes closed the entire time I patted him. Aunt Jeeb told me how the three dogs came to live at her house. Anut had been born there, the offspring of a former dog she loved dearly. Bobo kept begging at the gate until she let him in. But Pokey, Pokey was released into the world with the intention to die. He was small, a puppy about six inches long, and went from garbage heap to garbage heap. Other dogs chased him. Other dogs bit him. Aunt Jeeb found him near death, his leg broken, teeth marks on his body. She took him in, cared for him.

"They choose us," Aunt Jeeb said. "Even when we are not looking, they find us. Do you understand?"

Not really. But it did not matter because we sat there for a long while, the sun setting, the frogs croaking a night song, my hand moving to all three dogs until my mother and father came home, and the dogs rose in unison to bark at their arrival, even me, the new member of the pack.

ev

I forgot I was born in Chicago. Forgot that I was American. Forgot English. My other life eight thousand miles away began slipping away, like a dream. It didn't take long, a week really, and suddenly I was Thai, the most Thai I'd ever felt. My father would tell me to speak English, to show off my American tongue to his friends at the VW garage.

"Say elephant," he said.

"Chang!" I said.

"Say fish," he said.

"Pla!" I said.

"Say dog," he said.

"Mah!" I said.

A switch had been flipped, and the Thai part of me, which lay dormant for so long, freed itself. Where was America? Where was Illinois? Where was Chicago? Where was McVicker Avenue? Who cared? I was in Thailand, speaking rapid-fire Thai, answering the phone like my cousins, playing like a Thai boy ought to play.

Like saving that bumblebee.

Ant and I stomped the concrete—he in bare feet that collided with the pavement in muffled thuds, and I in bulky sneakers that slapped against the ground. The Thai sun was hot on our bare backs. The housedogs were perplexed, watching silly boys stomp like monkeys.

What were we doing? Trying to save a life that was as small as the tip of my thumb, a bumblebee. We stomped to keep the ants away. They were vicious, crawling from every angle—from under the parked Toyota, from the trunk of the banana tree, from the shadow of the looming house. My cousin used the wind from his step to propel the ants backwards. I stepped on them, leaving tiny balls of brown on the driveway. My cousin looked at me and cringed, probably wondering why his American-born cousin was so violent.

The wounded bumblebee moved along the driveway. It tried to buzz away, but there was only one wing. A couple of ants made it past our stomping feet and took little nibbles at the bee.

My cousin sighed. "It's moving slow," he said.

"Maybe it's hungry," I said.

Ant straightened himself. I stood only to his chest. When he stretched, I saw every bone of his ribcage, how his stomach sucked in. My stomach stuck out.

"What does a bee eat?" I asked.

"Something sweet," he said.

"Like cake?"

"Like soda."

I had an idea. I ran into the house and came out with a spoonful of syrupy red.

"What's that?" he said.

"Strawberry syrup."

I knelt down and pounded a couple ants with my palm, then put a small pool of syrup in the bee's path.

The bee veered in a different direction. The syrup made the ants greedier.

"Why won't it eat?" he said.

I put another pool right next to its head, impossible to ignore. The bee stopped. Placed its small mouth on the syrup and appeared to drink.

"You see?" I said. "You see how much the bee's drinking?"

Ant smiled, a gap in between his teeth.

We went back to stomping, working harder because ants came from all directions, different colors now, even the red ones that bit and peed.

When we noticed the bee again, it had died, head in the red. Ant went crying to Aunt Jeeb inside the house. I picked the bee up by its one good wing and thought about a traditional Thai funeral—burn the body and release its soul to heaven so it may buzz again with Buddha. My mother told me that was how Thai people treated the dead. We did not bury them in the ground; we did not enter a procession of cars that followed a hearse to a cemetery. No. We burned the body to ash.

I found an empty matchbox and put the dead bee in it. My cousin came out wet-eyed and asked what I was doing.

"Sending it to Buddha," I said.

We sat on our knees in the front garden, under the eucalyptus. A hibiscus vine twined around the trunk, its flowers dark yellow. Ant said it was fitting to bury the bee near the vine because he had seen the bumblebee—this bumblebee—drink from the cups of the flowers.

"This is where it belonged," he said.

We pressed our hands together and prayed. I prayed quickly, waiting to light the box on fire and watch the flames swallow the box. My cousin closed his eyes and tilted his head to the sky. His lips moved silently, as if he was whispering to the clouds.

ও

Most of my drawings were of Pokey. He stayed still the longest. Many consisted of him lying down, body curled into a C, head snuggled into his side. The more I drew, the more I discovered scars along his torso, nicks and gnashes along his legs and stomach. The very tip of his right ear was missing. He rarely moved, but when he did it was always because of a butterfly. He liked following them, his face tilted high at bushes, trotting a couple steps to get closer to them. I liked butterflies too, and tried to draw them, but they fluttered too fast away.

When no one was around, I talked to Pokey.

"Pokey," I'd say, "it's hot."

His tail would slice back and forth.

"Pokey," I'd say, "Are there mummies here?"

They weren't deep conversations, but they were important to a three-year old obsessed with monsters, a three-year old waiting for his cousins to return.

Pokey was my best friend. My first one. I had no friends in America, whatever that was, and most of the time I played alone at the park or at daycare. It was something my parents were trying to solve—this shyness. It was the reason they signed me up for extra-curricular activities at temple, but even there, I sought solitude instead of companionship. There was something unspoken between Pokey and me, something I could not name, but understood, even at that age. Friendship was an elementary concept between a boy and dog. It was a feeling. It was an unquestionable idea of loyalty. An unspoken pledge of protection.

Friendship, I believe, was the reason I was not bitten that afternoon. The servants opened the gates for one of my uncles and in walked a foreign dog. I had seen this dog before. Seen it bully other dogs in the neighborhood. Seen how the other dogs cowered and rolled over to show their stomachs when he came around. He was a mangy brown, a ridge running down his back. He had an air of superiority to him, like a guy at the bar with big muscles who knew he had big muscles. This dog was double the size of Pokey, thicker than Bobo. Aunt Jeeb called him the "mean one," and when she walked to the market, she carried a large stick to fend him away.

But that afternoon, he slipped in behind my uncle's pickup and went immediately for me, sitting on the marble deck, drawing Pokey, who was a few feet away. I hadn't noticed the other dog until Pokey rose up, the fur on his back raised, his teeth bared. From out of his mouth came a low growl, a sound I had not heard him make during my time with him. The mean one made the same sound, too, and for a second they stared at each other like boxers in the ring.

No one had noticed the other dog but Pokey and me. Not the servant girls, not my uncle, not Bobo or Anut. No one noticed until the fight. The mean one lunged at Pokey and Pokey lunged back, and it was the sound of bark and bite and snarl. I screamed. I could not do anything else. I sat five feet away from the fight, and I could feel fear creep into every extremity, and instead of fleeing, I could not move. They tumbled. They fell. I felt the wind of their movements. Bite. Snap. It didn't take long before the others came, Bobo and Anut. And then it was three against one, a chaotic collision of teeth and fur.

Aunt Jeeb used the garden hose.

The dogs dispersed, the mean one high-tailing it out of the gate.

What might've happened if Pokey was not there? Perhaps nothing. Perhaps the mean one was not mean at all. Perhaps he happened to be misnamed. Perhaps, really, he was the curious one. The unfortunate one. The wandering one. And perhaps Pokey wasn't protecting me at all. Perhaps, he was protecting his territory. This house. His spot on the cool marble deck.

But I like to think otherwise. Pokey protected me that day. That's how I would tell the story.

ℭ

My mother said we were going on a special outing. I would meet Grandfather Chua, and he would be happy to see me even if he didn't express his pleasure. Grandfather had been asking for me, but my mother couldn't bring herself to take me on her hospital visits because…because…. She never finished the sentence, but instead said Grandfather was the reason for my existence, all our existences. He was the one who insisted she go to America.

"Without his urging, there wouldn't be you," she said.

"What's America?" I said.

"Don't be silly."

We were speeding in a Toyota—always speeding—my cousin Oil beside me, holding my hand, my mother on the other side, holding the other.

Oil squeezed my hand like a heartbeat. She was my favorite cousin, despite being a girl. I wondered whether this was what it was like to have a sister, to have someone care for you, play with you, be your heartbeat. In the car, she wanted to know about America—whatever that was—and I told her lies.

"Does America have monkeys?" she said.

"Yes," I said. "They swing in apple trees."

"What's an apple?"

"A fruit."

"How do you say apple in Thai?"

"Apple."

We passed motorcycles and noodle carts. We passed temples and dilapidated homes. We passed fields of water lilies and fields of trash. Thailand was a land of the good and the bad, the poor and the rich, the beautiful and the ugly. We passed dogs, tons and tons of dogs.

"Grandfather is sick," Oil said.

"I was sick once," I said.

"Very sick," said Oil.

"Like the chicken pox?"

Oil shook her head. Her ponytail swung back and forth.

"Oil," my mother said, "Tell Tong about Grandfather."

"He coughs a lot," she said. "He walks with a stick and dogs follow him."

"Dogs?"

"Twenty dogs," she said. "He takes care of them. He names them by numbers."

"Why?" I said.

"It's easier to remember."

"What else?" my mother said.

"He likes to tell stories," Oil said.

Oil pointed to the Buddha around her neck. "He gave me this." The Buddha was small, copper, the size of a penny. I didn't have a Buddha yet, not for another three years, and I envied my cousin, who had her own, and I envied my father with five or six large ones around his neck, and I envied most of Thailand and their Buddhas.

"Are there dogs where we're going?" I asked.

"Probably not," Oil said. "No dogs in hospitals."

On the wall in our American home hung a black and white photo of my mother's entire family. My mother, ten at the time, and her four sisters and three brothers sat on the dirt ground around Grandfather. They wore traditional school uniforms, the girls with long skirts to the ankles and the boys in pressed slacks and short-sleeved shirts. Grandfather sat on a chair, chin raised with a pipe in his mouth.

My mother never spoke of him. Never mentioned his life or the importance of his life. Never mentioned the state of poverty they lived in, how her youth was spent in a small wooden shack with two rooms, how they lost their mother at a young age. Never mentioned how tirelessly Grandfather worked, a receptionist for a government official, how he saved enough money and bought shrimp farms my uncles eventually took over. Never spoke of how he put my mother through nursing school and the others through college, and because of him, they grew to be independent with families of their own. My mother never mentioned the dreams he had of Buddha, how Buddha told him to stop smoking—it would be his downfall—how Buddha came down on a lotus bud and said his oldest daughter should take that job as a nurse in America, how Buddha predicted a son.

The Toyota stopped.

Uncle Loon, the oldest of the family, waited outside the hospital. His shirt was stained and he looked like he hadn't slept much, red tracing his eyes. Still, he smiled and made an exasperated sound when he saw me, a sound that said I was so big and cute he couldn't stand it. He picked me up with one arm, offered Oil his other hand. "Father's waiting," he said.

Uncle Loon led us through the hospital, and before entering a room, he told Oil to wait outside. She nodded and sat in a waiting area as we entered.

"Father," Uncle Loon whispered.

On the bed lay a withered man, with IV needles in his arms

and a big clear tube in his mouth. His breaths were louder than the beepbeep of the machine beside the bed.

The man turned his head and blinked. A rough gurgle erupted from his throat, a laugh.

"Father, I brought my son," my mother said. She lifted me in front of her.

I did not believe the man was human. I hid my face against my mother's shoulder.

"This is your grandfather," my mother said. My mother guided my hand forward. I shook my head. "He will not hurt you," she said. The man's hand was a piece of wrinkled brown cloth covering bones. I took his hand. In that moment, the three of us were connected, generations melding at once. He had eyes like my mother's. He did not blink.

"Boy," I heard him say. "Strong," I heard him say.

Then he blinked. He turned his head away, releasing his hand from mine, and began coughing, a deep-lung cough. My mother put me down. Uncle Loon pulled me away, leading me out of the room, my mother staying behind.

Oil stood up and wiped away my tears with her finger.

"He was scary," I said.

"He's not always," she said.

"Let's go," Uncle Loon said.

Grandfather died shortly after my exit. He died while I clutched Uncle Loon's back and Oil clutched my back, and we whizzed through the cramped streets of Bangkok on a speedy motorcycle.

This was the last and only time I saw my grandfather, but my mother told me later that it wasn't. That I had gone to the hospital with her several times and I always cried, always squirmed out of her arms, always wanted to go home and play with the dogs, except this last time. She described a calm in that room that afternoon, a pervading stillness, as if the world settled for a second before continuing its rotation.

I don't remember that. I don't remember my grandfather other than that moment, that day, because it was linked to that motorcycle ride, the feeling of wind against my cheeks, Oil's arms around my waist, and the world speeding by in a loud roar.

♔

The day of my grandfather's funeral seemed to unravel itself in sepia, absent of light and pigment, dulled like the photo of the family taken that day, my mother and her siblings gathered around a black and white portrait of Grandfather, dressed in military garb, young, in his thirties. The family arranged themselves in the order of birth, but this time, the photo included their kids. My mother clutched me tight from behind, her arms draped over me, my cheeks red, my tie askew because of the heat. But most noticeable was the absence of smiles on the adults juxtaposed to the bright smiles of the kids. We knew nothing of sorrow, not yet. We knew nothing of pain. We knew nothing, really, of the hole in our parents' hearts. We only knew, like we had been taught time and again, that when a camera came out we were to smile, to show our happiness no matter what.

♔

Our family vacation was coming to an end. The next day, we would return to America, whatever that was, and we would not see Thailand and our relatives and the dogs for another two years. This would be the routine, our trips spaced out, time spilling by. I would return again when I was six and then nine and then twelve and then fourteen and then sixteen and so on and so on and so on. And with each return I would pick up where I left off, despite how old I'd become, despite my father absent on visits after I turned sixteen, despite the changes that would befall my family. I would fall in love with Thailand over and over, like first love, remember the heat and humidity like a tender embrace, the multitude of mosquito bites like painful kisses, the smell, the rhythm, the simplicity. I would fall in love with another dog and another dog and another dog. Some years, there would be one less relative. And some years there would be one less dog. And every year, Thailand would change, and my mother would talk about the change, and in her voice I would hear that longing to be part of that change. Each trip would be another beginning for me, not a continuation because continuation required an awareness of place and time and a closeness that I would never know. I was and forever would be the American-born Thai boy, someone on the outside, someone who came and went.

e∞

Pokey was nowhere to be found. He was not at breakfast. He did not come for his afternoon snack. He did not wander the grounds, did not bark at the usual things. I recalled Aunt Jeeb's story, remembered how Pokey was found with bite marks and a broken leg, and the thought of this happening again filled me with an overwhelming sense of dread.

I sat on the couch in the house. Gnats swirled around my head. A spider crawled up the white walls. My mother made me a plate of food—grilled chicken and sticky rice—and though this was my favorite meal, I could not eat it.

"Pokey," I said to myself.

A rustle.

I looked up. The sound seemed to come from behind me.

"Pokey," I said again.

Another rustle.

"Pokey."

Once more.

Behind the couch was a glass door no one ever used that led to a small alley between the house and retaining wall. Pokey looked up at me. He was curled into a tight little ball, his fur dull and almost gray, his eyes watery. I pushed open the door.

"Pokey," I said.

He salivated.

I reached out to touch him. I was not afraid to do this anymore. Pokey growled.

"Pokey," I said. "Where have you been?"

He growled again. I kept reaching.

"Pokey," I said. "Are you hungry?"

I went for the top of his head.

Pokey snapped at my fingers. His teeth clicked together. He squeaked when he moved, the sound scaring me even more. He snapped nowhere near my hands, probably a good two feet away, but I jerked away. The shock sent me crying.

My mother ran into the room. She checked my hands. "Did he get you?"

I shook my head.

"I told you not to touch dogs," she said. She stared down at Pokey, but instead of her expected anger, my mother's eyes furrowed together. She made the same sound when we watched a lion catch a baby gazelle on nature shows, of pity for a cruel, cruel world. She called for Aunt Jeeb.

I pointed at Pokey, made sure my hand was far from him. Aunt Jeeb sighed, knelt down behind the couch. Pokey whimpered. He tried to get up, but couldn't. Aunt Jeeb rested her hand on his neck. He let her. His stomach went in and out, his breath, loud snorts through the nose.

"Maybe he's hungry," I said.

"Maybe," she said.

I gave her my chicken and sticky rice. She thanked me and put the plate by Pokey's head. Pokey lifted his head, looked at the food, and then looked at us.

"Geen," Aunt Jeeb said. Eat.

I let go of my mother's hand and went to stand next to my aunt. "Pokey, eat."

Pokey stared.

"Eat," I said.

Not seconds after my aunt set the food down, the ants came. She took the food away. She closed the door.

"Why won't he eat?" I asked.

"He's not feeling well," Aunt Jeeb said. "Have to go to hospital."

"Like Grandfather?"

"Similar," said my mother.

One of my uncles loaded Pokey into the back of the pickup. Aunt Jeeb told me I should say good-bye to him. Said, because I was leaving early tomorrow, I might not have another chance. I looked over the truck bed. Pokey lay on some blankets, his head cushioned. I wanted to touch him, but I was afraid he'd snap again.

That afternoon, the boy I was said good-bye to the first dog he truly loved. The boy would cry and cry after the pickup truck pulled away, Pokey's head looking over the bed, bouncing to the bumps in the road, then turning and leaving and disappearing. The boy would cry again on the plane, while his mother held him close to her chest, saying they would return, they would see Pokey again, they would see everyone again. But they wouldn't, and she knew it.

That afternoon, the man I would become said good-bye to his grandfather, a man he remembered meeting once, and Pokey was my grandfather, in blankets, in the back of a pickup. I said good-bye to my grandfather, and the next morning I would be heading back to America, back to our suburban home in Chicago, back to our way of life, though on that plane, I had forgotten all about it, forgotten nearly everything, because that Thai boy did not want to let go. He wanted to hang on as long as he could.

Yummy

Fourth grade, Mrs. Sullivan's class, and Todd Capca tells me he watched something on TV that disturbed him to the core. "To the core, I tell you." Todd Capca is known for his theatrics, a skinny kid with flexible wrists and perfect brown hair. He will come out years later, but we are at the age where the word "gay" does not take shape, where Todd Capca is just a boy with flexible wrists and an extensive vocabulary.

At recess, Todd Capca has the ability to gather a crowd with his stories. That's how you locate him. Look for a crowd. Look for the skinny, perfect-hair, flexible-wristed boy in the center of the crowd. Look and listen to how he speaks, which is presidential. Like the day, for instance, when he approaches me on the park bench near the rusty rocking horses where I spend most of my time watching the clouds above take the shapes of my favorite animals—panther, elephant, dragon.

"So Ira," he says, elongating the "I" in my name. "Over the weekend I was watching a program on TV."

His hands are going, his flexible wrists bending this way and that. The boys in our class gather around, buzzards waiting for the kill. I know what will come out of Todd Capca's mouth will be insulting, so I try not to look at him but at the lumpy tar pavement of the playground.

"Something about China," Todd says. "That's where you're from, right?"

He doesn't wait for me to correct him, to say I am Thai. He knows I won't.

"That's right, China," Todd Capca says. "I learned a good deal about where you come from, Ira. Very informative, indeed." He indeed says "indeed," says it in that declarative and powerful way, like Ronald Reagan at the podium.

"I learned, for example, that China is the biggest country in the world and has the largest population. Did you guys know that?"

Someone says, "Wow," sarcastically.

"The Chinese have a ton of languages, and the languages seldom sound the same. We're lucky. In America, English is just English. Isn't it, guys?"

Someone says, "Yeah."

Someone says, "Chinese sounds like Chinese to me."

"And get this," Todd says, "the Chinese invented noodles. I love noodles. You guys love noodles?"

Someone says, "Love them, Todd."

"Really informative program," Todd Capca says. He takes a seat next to me. I can feel his skinny denim leg against mine, his smirk burning into the right side of my face.

"I learned other things, too." He shakes his head, and his perfect hair does not move.

Someone says, "Tell us what else you learned, Todd."

I look up at the sky. See a turtle lumbering by, then a dolphin, then a dog.

"Guys," says Todd Capca, "China is not like the great states we live in. There's a lot of poverty. Lots of people with no homes and living on top of each other."

Someone says, "That's a shame."

"It is," Todd Capca says. "It really is a shame. Imagine all those people who don't bathe, who don't brush their teeth. Dirty, dirty people crammed in together."

Someone says, "Dirtiest."

Todd Capca puts his arm around me. It's light, like bones, yet heavy enough I can't shake it off. "And these people, your people, Ira, are communists." Todd raises his eyes to the crowd of boys. "You guys know what communists are, right?"

Someone says, "The Russians."

Someone says, "Evil."

Todd Capca nods. "Afraid so. But that's not all." Todd Capca puts a finger up, smiles, and if there is anything more infuriating than his immovable hair, it's his white teeth in that wide mouth. "Your people," Todd Capca says, "and this fact disturbs me to the core, I tell you. Your people eat dogs."

Someone says, "Really?"

Someone says, "Gross."

"But true," Todd Capca says, and his voice is directed to the crowd now. "In China they eat dogs. Don't they, Ira?"

He doesn't wait for me to say anything because I won't.

"You see, guys, they tie the dog up, kill it, gut it, and stew it. The TV said so."

Someone says, "Stay away from my dog, Ira."

Someone says, "Don't even think about it, Fat Boy."

Someone says, "Egg rolls with a side of dog, please."

Todd Capca has belittled me again. I allow him. I'm good at it. He sticks his chin out and smiles that smile. The other boys go on about dogs. How can my people do such a thing? they say. They're going to tell their parents about this, they say. They say so-and-so is missing a dog and they bet Ira ate it.

I don't utter a word. My mind, however, turns and turns. My people do not eat dogs because my people aren't Chinese. We're Thai. I'm American. I eat like the rest of you—chicken, beef, pork. In fact, most of my meals are at the McDonald's a block away. Even when I have dinners at home dog meat is never served. Still, what Todd Capca has said affects me on a deep level, and I can't seem to get the image out of my mind, people eating dogs. My best friend Mike, who is in the other fourth grade class, the better one, has a rambunctious black lab named Boo, who always knocks me over with his paws and licks the sides of my face. How can you look at Boo and go "yummy"?

The lunch moms blow their whistles, signifying the end of recess. The whistle disrupts the talk of dog eating, but only briefly. For the next two years I will be known as Dog Eater. It's another nickname I add to a slew of others that usually begin with the word fat. We all head toward the school, me lagging behind and Todd Capca and his immovable hair beside me, smirking the entire way. He likes to see me suffer, likes to see the effect of his words. It makes him feel that power, I'm sure, we all want, that ability to exert some dominance over someone, because—years from now, for gay Todd Capca—this power will dissipate, and he will be like me, the one looking at the sky, the one who can't seem to find a shape in the clouds no matter how hard he stares.

☙

If I was older and in the age of the Internet, I would have gone online and searched out the answer to whether people ate dogs, and I would have found what I was looking for in seconds: Yes. In countries like China, Korea, Philippines. Yes. In countries like Taiwan, Indonesia, Malaysia. Yes. In countries like France, Mexico, Switzerland. Yes. In the Artic and Antarctic. Yes. In the United States.

Dogs were eaten in China in the time of Confucius; writing from the Zhou Dynasty suggested that dog was considered one of the "three beasts" besides pig and goat bred for food, and that dog was the tastiest of the three.

Dog meat is best cured for jerky or stewed till tender, and in Taiwan it was called the "fragrant" meat.

In 1910 the Council of Veterinary School of Belgium recommended dog meat as human food.

Pet dogs were rarely eaten, only dogs farmed to be food, as Cortes discovered in the markets among the Aztecs sometime in 1519.

Even in the "great states" dog meat was put into sausages till about 1845, hence "hot dogs," and in the nineteenth century a dog meat diet was used as a possible cure for tuberculosis.

There are more facts about dog meat, more interesting tidbits about eating dog, but I did not know any of this then. I only knew the thought of eating a dog terrified me, saddened me, made me hate myself even more if it was true. The source of this hate was unfounded, but it seemed to me that I was close to the Chinese; my ancestors were Chinese. My skin was their shade. My food was similar. It was not out of the realm of possibility for Thais to eat dogs. Was it? Already, I was growing to despise the color of my skin and the oddities associated with my family. Why couldn't they speak English? Why did they pack weird lunches, like fried rice or garlic-oil ramen noodles? Why did my mother insist I wear a Buddha around my neck instead of a cross?

George Orwell wrote in *Animal Farm*: "All animals are equal, but some animals are more equal than others." A dog, I believed, would be one of those animals. So I clung to the possibility that Todd Capca was wrong. That Todd Capca made the entire thing up. I was nine. I was learning my way through this weird world of white people, and Todd Capca was the quintessential weird white person, and though I hated him, I wanted to be like him, too—to possess his intellect, his hair, his ability to tell a story.

And it was a story, wasn't it? A fiction. A tale.

⁓

I am at the dinner table at the usual time of 5:30, and my mother has just instructed me to drink two full glasses of water. It's a routine she enforces, standing over me as I guzzle down each tall cup. Her theory: Drinking two glasses of water will make me eat less, which in turn, will make me less fat. What happens: I drink too fast and too sloppy, sloshing water on the table and all over my front. What happens: I eat too much anyway just to spite her.

I hate this routine, but my mother won't give me my fried rice with Oscar Meyer hot dogs if I don't do it. Today, however, I'm not hot on eating hot dogs. The mention of anything dog makes me squirm. When my mother puts the plate of rice in front of me, I start segregating the hot dogs onto the left side of the plate. This, to her, is unusual behavior from her only son, who if asked what his favorite meal is, would always say nuked hot dogs and jasmine rice.

"What's the matter?" my mother says in Thai.

"Nothing," I say.

"Nothing is not nothing," she says.

I shrug. Stab a hot dog.

My mother takes care to make the hot dogs presentable. It's one of the only meals she can cook. She cuts them into inch-long segments and makes an X at the tip of one end, so when the hot dogs cook they flower open. I know it pains her to see me mistreating her culinary artistry. I know by the way she sits heavily in the chair next to me with a scowl etched on her face.

"I want to know," she says, "why you're not eating."

"Mie hue," I say. Not hungry.

She guilts me to eat. She speaks of the starving Ethiopian children and the flies buzzing around their mouths and eyes, and how this one meal, this one meal with the flowered hot dogs, would sustain those starving children for a week.

"What do you think about that?" she says.

"I wonder if Ethiopians eat dogs," I say.

My mother tilts her head. Her glasses dangle at her chest, and she puts them on to look at me, as if to make sure that the boy in front of her is still her son. Her son does not play with his food but devours it. Her son does not ask odd questions during dinnertime.

"Ethiopians don't eat," she says. "That's the point."

"Do Thai people eat dogs?"

"Crazy," she says, but she doesn't sound convincing. She doesn't sound like she often does when I ask her silly questions. Her voice is without exasperation. It is without impatience.

"Do we?" I ask.

My mother takes her time. She picks up my fork and plunges it into a hot dog then puts it into her mouth and chews it gingerly. "We don't," she says.

And there's a sense of relief, a sense that the world isn't nonsensical as it seems, not like *Alice in Wonderland* or *Charlie and the Chocolate Factory*, two books I devoured a couple of days before, two books that defied logic and rationality.

"But some do." My mother stabs another hot dog.

My throat closes. I look down at my hands, trying to hide the wetness seeping into my eyes. I want to weep for all the dogs found on dinner plates.

My mother nods. Eats another piece of hot dog. "You eat what you have, and sometimes, you have very little."

"But a dog?"

"Yes."

"Really?"

"Yes."

"But why?"

"I already told you."

"But why?"

My mother doesn't know how to explain this. How does she convey the complexities of poverty? How does she talk about hunger? How does she explain desperateness? How does she say the world is cruel to some people, and no matter what they do, they can't have a McDonald's down the street, they don't have a working kitchen or a sink with running water? How does she explain that dogs are eaten in small villages in the Northeast Isaan area of Thailand and among hill tribes of the north? How does she explain a different set of value systems, way of living and way of a life?

Jonathan Safran Foer's book *Eating Animals* questions why we choose to eat pig and not dog, when the pig possesses as much intelligence and feeling as any canine. Foer states comically: "… [Dogs] are remarkably unremarkable…." and yet what we discover is the fact that eating dog is taboo in contemporary America. Elsewhere around the world, however, this notion is not. This notion is culturally acceptable.

Except, I can't accept it.

This is like the word "gay." It doesn't fully form in the mind of a nine-year-old, who loves dogs, who at one point wanted one so badly he created a dog companion as a best friend. This notion doesn't make sense because sense is shaped by experience, and experience is shaped by time. And my time has been spent in this suburban house with this family, this mother, who cooks hot dogs that blossom in oil and heat.

My mother does not know how to explain this. So she doesn't.

She eats all my hot dogs instead.

She eats my rice.

I don't complain.

This I understand: She eats for the starving Ethiopian children. I don't to save the dogs.

Sensitive Boy

Before the end of my parents' marriage, I couldn't stop reading. I read everything—junk mail, Sears catalogs, magazines and textbooks, canned food labels, cereal boxes, street signs and billboards. If it had words on it, I'd read it. I inherited this from my mother, who on road trips read mundane things endlessly. It was her way of passing time, of learning a language she feared. I understood my mother's impulse. If you verbalized the word, it would gain meaning. So, I, too, read anything, until finally English made deeper sense. I felt as if I'd become one of the X-Men, a comic book series I read voraciously, and my new mutant superpower—reading—gave me control over my life. I no longer struggled with multisyllabic words like onamonapeia or cornucopia or indigestible. My brain calculated the breaks in nanoseconds, and the tongue and voice corresponded just as quickly. I no longer found myself stuck between two languages—Thai or English.

Before this moment, I'd hit the language wall mid-sentence. This wall was like a magician placing a black veil over his trick, only he never took the veil off. I'd be stuck, sifting for the appropriate word in a given situation. At times, Thai slithered out unexpectedly. My white friends, Mike and Kevin, called these moments "Thai time."

Thai time happened the day I confessed my love to Kristen Gildea, the new girl down the street. Kristen moved to Oak Lawn in the beginning of the school year and became every sixth-grade boy's crush. She was pretty in a plain way and had a voice that was soothing, like the touch of velvet. I noticed her because I was riding my bike back and forth down the block, and she waved at me. A cute girl never waved at me. I tried to impress her by doing a wheelie, but I lost control of the bike and swerved into an oak tree. Her mother bandaged the scrape on my knee, and Kristen Gildea became a friend.

Each morning, Kristen and I walked to school together, both of us patrol guards, wearing bright orange sashes across the front of our clothes. We usually talked about TV, and once she laughed when I told her *Moonlighting* was my favorite show. "My mom watches that," she said. "It's kinda for old people, isn't it?" I wanted to tell her it wasn't. I wanted to tell her I watched it because of the love part, because of David (Bruce Willis) and Maddie (Cybil Shepherd) and their first kiss in a parking garage, a collision of lips. I wanted to tell Kristen Gildea that I imagined kissing her like that—in a moment of passion, no questions asked or answered. I imagined this often, as often as I imagined being a superhero.

Kristen became my first friend of the opposite sex. Something told me that I was slipping into a pattern of friendship with her. I could tell by the way we talked and walked, could tell by the casualness of it all. She began asking me about the other boys in class, where they lived, what they liked to do in Oak Lawn, Illinois. She expressed how she wasn't all into the mullet haircut and liked boys who were clean cut. "Kinda like you," she said, which made my inside twist, "and like Matt," which did not.

In the waiting room of a doctor's office, I read a woman's magazine. My mother had gone in for a checkup, and I remember a bit of what the article said. Don't let friendship ruin a possible romance. Get out of the friend zone. Pump up your game. I'm paraphrasing badly, and there were other tips like how to make it hotter in bed—which I assumed was a blanket buying guide— but that article made me think that I indeed had to pump up my game, whatever that meant.

It was fall. The neighborhood was littered with leaves, and the Lake Michigan clouds were gathering over the neighborhood. Nerves made my hands tremble, my voice tremble. I bought a candy bar at the gas station, and wore my Bugle Boy sweater with patches on the front—the new trend in late eighties fashion. I knocked on Kristen's door, and she emerged with those dimpled cheeks I wanted to put my fingers in.

"Hey," she said.

"Hi," I said.

"What's up?" she said.

I thrust the candy bar at her with both hands, like an offering to a monk, and said in a rushed breathy voice, "I chaub you."

Kristen's forehead furrowed. "What?"

"Chun chaub you."

"What?"

"Chun like cune."

"I don't understand," Kristen said. Her arms were folded across her chest. She waited for me to say something sensible, but I was fresh out of sensible. My brain flipped and re-flipped words. Nothing connected. Nothing I could voice.

I did what I thought I should do in moments like this. I ran. I ran down the block. I ran home. I ran up the stairs and into my room, slamming the door behind me. There I stayed the rest of the night. There I ate the candy bar meant for Kristen. There I would stay for the following weeks, after Kristen agreed to be Matt Menegheni's girlfriend. There, in order to forget the heaviness in my heart, I read.

↳

In Richard Wright's memoir, *Black Boy*, Wright found himself confused and angry about where he stood as a black man in a white world. It was reading that unlocked his brain. "I hungered for books, new ways of looking and seeing. It was not a matter of believing or disbelieving what I read, but of feeling something, of being affected by something that made the look of the world different." Like Wright, reading connected me to place, made me feel less alien, less inhibited. With knowledge of words came knowledge of self-worth. I began believing in myself in ways I hadn't before, began understanding the intricacies of the human heart, the complexities that existed in our lives. I wondered, for example, why my father did not return from work at the usual time, 11:30 p.m. I wondered why he no longer checked on me as I slept, but headed straight for the telephone. I knew he was not speaking to my mother, who worked the night shift at Oak Forest Hospital, because of the playful lilt in his voice, the soft flirtatious whisper, followed, at times, by muted laughter.

Before this, we were a family of routine. I walked the same route to school, with the same people, and arrived at the same time. I ate dinner at the same table, in the same chair, utilizing the same plate, drinking water from the same Star Wars glass. My mother woke up at the same time and got ready for work at 8:30 p.m. on the dot, and she exited the house at exactly at 9. I watched the same TV shows, brushed my teeth in the same way, went to the bathroom at roughly the same time. On Mondays and Wednesdays, I took Tae Kwon Do lessons. On Tuesdays and Thursdays, tennis lessons at the racquet club. My mother sewed at the same sewing machine, overlooking the same neighborhood, listening to the same Thai folk music cassette tape. She sewed only two types of clothes: nurse uniforms or elaborate Thai dresses. Change was something we did not take to well. It affected the rhythm of our day, my mood. This was how my immigrant family operated. We followed schedules because schedules were dependable, schedules gave us direction, schedules were safe.

Change, however, was the part of life I was entering. At Harnew, the boys stayed with Mr. Turek, our sixth grade teacher, and the girls went with the school nurse. The boys watched a silly film about penises and vaginas, which we secretly giggled about, but kept silent because Mr. T scared us with his overly husky voice and his ability to give detentions. The girls came back quiet and tight-lipped, faces pale as specters.

Change was also the thought of girls, like Kristen Gildea, creeping into my consciousness. Change was my voice. Change was the hair growing above my lip and other areas. Change. Change. Change.

Books eased me into this transitional time. In books, the world was different each day. In *The Lion, the Witch, and the Wardrobe*, the Pevensie siblings crawled into a wardrobe and entered a fantastical land, becoming kings and queens. Jack Torrance in *The Shining* transformed from father to deranged lunatic, trying to murder his family. Or Louis, the voiceless swan in *The Trumpet of the Swan*, laid hands on the trumpet that changed his life.

One night, my father came home at the usual time. I read in bed, leaning against the wall, Buddha above me. My touch lamp was on, *A Wrinkle in Time*, a book for school, opened on my lap. I was so caught up in the book I did not hear my father come home, or perhaps, I had become accustomed to another routine, one where he didn't return.

"Boy," he said.

I looked up. Smiled, surprised to see him.

"You're up," he said.

"You're home," I said.

He wore a magenta shirt and gray slacks, pens plugged into the shirt pocket. I noticed he hadn't shaved, the fuzz around his face darker, fuller.

"Reading?"

I nodded.

"Always reading."

I shrugged.

"Good book?"

Yes, it was, but I couldn't explain how good the book was to my father, how the characters used something called a tesseract to jump from one planet to the next, how the main character Meg Murry was falling for her friend Calvin O'Keefe. I couldn't explain any of this because reading was a private act, something separate from my family. This was true, I would learn, for most people. It was the reason we sought quiet spots to ourselves—the lonely nook, the uninhabited couch, the empty room or park bench. In this way, we give ourselves over, letting go of the world we are tethered to, and allowing our brains to wander elsewhere.

I shrugged.

"Chicken wings?" my father said. He raised a greasy paper bag; the roomed smelled oily and heavenly.

Friday nights were chicken wings with my father, a routine we kept from my mother, who would hate to know I ate after I brushed my teeth, hate to know I ate. But it was more than that. It was time with a man I rarely saw during the week because of work and school. It was time to be in his presence, to stare at him and think this is the man I want to become despite his oddities, to think this man loved me because he found time to buy chicken wings on the way back from work from a hole-in-wall dive on Archer Avenue, a neighborhood known for muggings and gang violence. And these wings, these wings were the best wings in Chicago, possibly the world, with their crispy coating, that audible crunch at first bite, the salt and pepper simplicity that assaults the tongue, the spurt of sizzling juice that steams the mouth. Oh how I looked forward to them at the beginning of each week, reminding my father on his evening phone calls home not to forget, to buy more than the usual ten because I would be hungry. And when he returned home, I would have the TV trays pulled out in the usual spots—he on the barcalounger, me on the chair my mother stole from the nurse's dorm a decade ago—the napkins ready, two large glasses of water wet with condensation. And there we'd sit in front of the TV, watching some bad cop show. There we'd eat, father and son, man and boy, and sometimes we'd talk, but mostly we'd be silent, enjoying this hour before going to bed, fatigue finally overcoming us, our fingers scented with chicken, our mouths messy with grease.

"No thanks," I said and returned my eyes to the book.

Wright wrote: "But I could not conquer my sense of guilt, my feeling that the white men around me knew that I was changing . . . ." It was Guilt that sat heavy on my shoulders that night. Guilt that blurred Madeleine L'Engle's prose into incoherency, Guilt like an accusatory finger. But this was also true: sometimes change hurts. Sometimes change defines what will happen, what is inevitable. Change, sometimes, is sacrifice of the thing we love most.

༅

The only place I wanted to be besides my room was the library. I had been there a few years before, part of a Cub Scouts field trip. I remember being surrounded by books, remember the hypnotic trance I was in as I walked the cramped aisles. The floor of the library was stained and moldy. The concrete walls were cracked; the fluorescent lights flickered. That mattered very little. What did matter was this sensation that took hold of me, the rush, the high of being around so many books. I carried this high with me, and at times, even now, I feel the overwhelming desire to be in a bookstore or library, to be immersed in paperbacks and hardcovers. I'd run my hand along their spines. My eyes would speed through titles and authors. And there'd be the smell: the musk of paper.

There was no better world than one filled with books—mountains of books, prairies of books, oceans of books. This would be the landscape of my dreams, a world in which there was a new story every day.

My father did not read. I do not count the multiple volumes of astrological grids for his side job as a fortune teller or the chemical equations in his notebook for the perfect floor tile. I don't count the numerous times he flipped through a golf magazine, and even then, I'm sure he was only looking at the photos. A book in my father's hand would have been as alien to me as seeing him in anything other than pleated slacks and golfing polos. He was a man who, when he wasn't working at the tile factory in south Chicago, when he wasn't at the golf course, could be found planted in front of a television, watching bad made-for-TV movies.

What an anomaly I must have been to him, this pudgy-fingered boy of his who buried his nose in books and would seldom respond to anything. This boy could spend hours without uttering a word, could be so absorbed by a book he wouldn't even notice the presence of his father, a man he so admired and loved, watching him from the couch. Don't get me wrong; this boy loved TV, too, but at that time, he loved the written word a little more, needed it.

Which was why it was peculiar when I asked if I could get a library card, that my father would want one, too.

It was Saturday, and my father walked up to the library counter, me trailing behind. The librarian was Kristen Gildea's mother. My heart still hurt. Hurt when I thought of Kristen and Matt holding hands after school, Kristen and Matt trading lunches, Kristen and Matt etching their name on the park bench I liked sitting on. My cheeks flushed, my legs went weak. I felt like I would tumble face-first into the library's dirty carpet. I wondered if Kristen told her mother about that afternoon. Told her how I spoke an alien language and then ran away. Told her how the past week I walked to school without her and how I turned the other way when she said hello. I wondered all this, feeling that familiar urge to flee again. But I was with my father, who possessed a fearless way about him. It was why he was promoted to supervisor at the tile factory, why he had power over so many other men, why it didn't scare him to speak to white people, unlike my mother. In this way, my father was like Atticus Finch, the protagonist of *To Kill a Mockingbird*, a man who didn't run from adversity, who stood his ground no matter what.

Whether Kristen's mother knew of anything, she did not let on. She just smiled, fingers laced in front of her. She didn't look like other mothers on the southside, not the over-smoked, pudgy ones. Kristen's mother looked like an older version of her daughter—luxurious brown hair that was kept in a loose bun; rosy cheeks on a pale complexion.

She knew me instantly. "Ira," she said. "It's so nice to see you." She bent over the counter and offered me her hand.

My father accepted it for me. "You know my boy?"

Kristen's mother smiled. "He's in the same class as my daughter. We live down the street."

"My son," my father said and stuck out his chest, "he like to read. Smart boy. Smarter than his papa." He laughed, high-pitched and echoing. It was like an alarm in the quiet of the library. I stood away from my father. I knew what he was doing. I knew he was trying to impress this American stranger in front of him, this pretty American stranger.

Kristen's mother, taken aback by my father's laugh, straightened a bit. I could tell, even then, that she wanted to shush him, wanted to tell him to quiet down so he didn't bother the other patrons, but his jovialness, his apparent lack of understanding of where he was and the rules that existed made her hesitant. How do you tell a foreign man who wasn't strong with English, a man who was doing nothing wrong but being happy, to quiet down? These situations happened often, at other places, and they were always awkward.

"Let me tell you something funny," my father said, leaning in, as if imparting a secret. "I say to him, 'Boy, want some ice cream?' and you know what he say?"

Kristen's mother played along and shook her head.

"He say, 'I'm reading.' Any other kid, they drop the book and then they messy with ice cream. Not Ira. He messy with books." My father laughed again.

Kristen's mother looked at me and winked, as if she knew exactly what I was feeling at that moment. Her smile, like Kristen's, put me at ease, made me feel understood. Or perhaps she detected in my father's voice pride, that, yes, he was boasting, but he was boasting out of love.

She looked at my father again. "How can I help you?"

"Ira, he want a card."

"Library card?"

"Exactly."

"No problem."

Kristen's mother gave my father a form to fill out, which he handed directly to me without even looking at it. It was a standard form, asking standard information, making sure I understood late fees and renewal restrictions. I signed it, and within a couple minutes, Kristen's mother handed me the first laminated card I ever owned. Having a card made me feel like I had broken into the ranks of adulthood.

"What book would you like to check out?" Kristen's mother said.

I looked around. There were so many books. That book high was returning.

"Would you like a suggestion?" she said.

I nodded.

Kristen's mother took out a book from the return bin. "Just came back today. It's great." She handed me the book. It had a picture of a dog on the cover.

I read it. "*Old Yeller.*"

"Classic," she said.

My father said, "I would like one, too."

"What?" I said and covered my mouth.

"You read?" Kristen's mother said. It was a presumptive question, I realize now, that a man like my father, a Thai man who spoke English with missing verbs, could read. But I like to think Kristen's mother was onto my father, that she recognized at first glance that he was a talker and not a reader.

"I read everything," said my father. "Ira get reading from me. I teach him."

I tried not to shake my head. To say anything contrary was to make my father lose face in front of an American. To lose face was to lose dignity. To lose face was a sign of vulnerability.

My father eyed a few books on the shelf closest to him. He strolled over to one and picked it out. I don't remember the name of the book, but I remember the thickness, the girth and weight that made my father use two hands to put it on the counter. I like to think it was *War and Peace* or *Ulysses.*

"You would like to check that out?" Kristen's mother said, titling her head. I, too, was tilting my head, tilting it so far the world looked sideways.

"Yes."

She stamped the back of the book, hesitated before handing it over to him. "Three weeks and then you have to return it, OK?"

"Absolutely," my father said. "I bring it back in three days," which he didn't. He never brought the book back, never opened it, never touched it for four years. It was part of the things he left behind, like much of his clothes, his photos, his buckets and buckets of golf balls. When I cleaned out his closet after he moved out, I found the book. Dusty and heavy as a cinder block. I returned it. I paid the fine, which was more expensive than the book itself.

ℕ

"Beauty of whatever kind," Edgar Allan Poe wrote, " . . . invariably excites the sensitive soul to tears." I was that sensitive soul Poe described. I remember this. I remember this because my mother a couple of years ago reminded me how hard and long I cried about everything. In her childhood stories about me, I'm always crying, always hyperventilating, my cheeks tear-streaked and stained. "Sensitive boy," she'd say with a hint of wistfulness. I wonder whether she tells these stories to embarrass me or because she wants to remind me of who I was and how I responded to the world I did not understand, whether she misses that boy and his tears, the boy who came to her for everything.

I stopped crying when my father left. I detached myself from feeling, like him, who I remember during the worst of my parents' arguments sat motionless, while my mother berated him for his infidelity. I carried an invective against tears. I was quick to point out how crying never truly conveyed hurt. What were tears, I would say, but a biological reaction, a way of protecting eyes from debris? Good actors can produce them at will. Slews of high-schoolers cry in melodramatic fashion in the hallways of OLCHS. But if asked what they truly felt, they couldn't form any words. They were empty. They were fake. Tears, after all, were not language.

I missed that boy my mother spoke of, though. I missed him because he felt so easily. He did not trap things inside. He wept with the force of a storm.

I recall watching *Little House on the Prairie* when I was five or six. I don't remember what the episode was about. I didn't understand what was going on—the English too fast, the content too difficult to comprehend—but the music, epically orchestrated, ripped at me. The images on our old Zenith—swaying golden grass and expansive blue sky filled with bulbous white clouds—and of the characters—remorseful faces streaked red, faces pulled down with sorrow—sat heavy on my chest. The combination of these things put sadness, like a rock, in my heart.

Or the day I finished *Old Yeller*, reading it as soon as I arrived home from the library.

Imagine Sensitive Boy reading this novel about a dog. Imagine how he flipped page to page, in love with the writing, with the simplicity of the sentences, in love immediately with this dog, even though he is not described as handsome at all. "He was a big ugly slicked-hair yeller dog. One short ear had been chewed clear off and his tail had been bobbed so close to his rump that there was hardly stub enough left to wag." And yet, the boy could not find fault with this dog, because he felt he understood this dog and his imperfections. Sensitive Boy was not a handsome boy. He was never described as such. Sensitive Boy was described as sensitive, as Chubby, as Fat, as Gook, as Oriental, as Chink. Sensitive Boy loved too easily, and in the midst of this love, his heart broke too easily. Because of this, Old Yeller became real. Sensitive Boy could feel him under his hand, his coarse fur, could feel his wet nose. Old Yeller rescued Sensitive Boy, like he rescued Travis Coates and his family.

Sensitive Boy needed to be rescued.

My father was upstairs, watching golf. He came to check on me, my nose so close to the book.

"Boy," he said, "Back away a little bit."

I did.

"Boy," he said. "Are you crying?"

I was.

"Boy," he said. "Why are you crying?"

I did not have an answer.

My Heart. Open.

My father wanders. It is his nature. His wanderings are accidental. He is not the lone wolf type. Wanderers like that are predictable. You know they won't stay long; you expect nothing from them. He is more like my cocker spaniels on a walk. Their attentive tails pointed like fingers, their noses hovering over the ground like veering wayward vacuums.

This wandering nature is the reason he left Thailand and his first family. It is the reason he found his way to America, illegally. It is the reason he eventually left our family. One can only live so long this way. Eventually time catches up. Eventually what you left behind comes haunting back. Eventually you realize you don't know where you are.

⁀

My father reappeared two years after the divorce, during the summer of 1995. I was back at home for summer break, working at a camera store to feed my nicotine habit and obsessive need to eat at Applebee's. My mother answered the phone and then promptly dropped it on the kitchen table. "For you," she said and walked out of the room.

I knew instantly it was him.

When I heard his voice, I laughed, the way my mother laughed at inappropriate moments, like funerals, the news of her father's terminal illness, her lost dreams. This was another something we shared. With my father on the line, I laughed when I wanted so badly to say "fuck you" in a clear, crisp voice, my consonants clicking after the first word.

"How have you been?" he said.

"Good."

"In college?"

"Yep."

"Studying hard?"

"Yep."

"How's your mother?"

"Good."

"I miss you," he said.

"Yeah."

"I want to know about your life."

"OK."

"Just OK?"

"Yeah."

"Are you working?"

"Yeah."

"Good money?"

"Sure."

"I miss you."

"Good."

"I'm not working anymore."

"OK."

"My heart isn't good."

"OK."

"Lay off."

"Yeah."

"They want to look at my heart," he said.

"Yeah."

"Open me up."

"OK."

"I won't let them."

"Yeah."

"I don't want to die."

"OK."

"You want to have lunch next week?" he said.

No would have been the easiest answer. No, I could've said, because I have pushed you out of my mind, out of my life. No, because when I get drunk with friends I vilify you, curse you, say things I wouldn't while sober. No, because Mom and I did everything we could to erase all reminders of you in the house, all the clothes you didn't take, your razor, your toothbrush, your fortune-telling books, all thrown out.

But no matter what we did, my father was there. He would always be there. His absence was a shadow over us all.

"Sure," I said.

"You like duck. I remember how much you like duck. I know a place."

And next week came and I waited by the window for the station wagon. When it pulled up, I dashed to get into the car. Looking back at the house, I saw my mother at the window, her eye in the sliver of the curtain, and I knew she would be at that exact spot when I returned.

℘

My dogs live by routine. They eat twice a day. Breakfast at seven and dinner at five thirty. In the hours between, they munch on Milkbones. Each day, they go through the dog door numerous times and see the same yard, perhaps the same tormenting squirrel. They bark at the same neighbors, and mark the same places. Most of the day, they sleep in their favorite spots. They have become accustomed to this life, and if anything disrupts it—late dinner or the dog door closed because the lawn people are working outside—they stress. They wander restlessly from room to room. They bark at the slightest sounds. They stare unflinchingly at me, as if begging for me to make the world right again.

The world wasn't right. My father had come back, and we were sitting in a restaurant in Lemont staring at each other. He kept saying how much I'd grown, how I resembled my mother, how I needed a shave. He had taken me to an old-school Chinese restaurant, where roast ducks and soy-sauce chickens hung on hooks by their slender necks. Around us, people slurped giant bowls of noodle soup, shoved rice into their greasy mouths. The butcher blade thumped endlessly on meat. In large steel pots, broth boiled and bubbled. This was my favorite type of restaurant. I hated my father for knowing me well.

I hated him even more for leaving us, for being unfaithful. I planned on telling him what I'd kept inside and asking him the questions I needed answered—Did you really cheat on Mom? Were we not good enough for you? Where were you for so long? But the man across from me, wearing a purple oxford I had outgrown in the sixth grade, wasn't the same father. His shoulders slouched forward, his back bent as if he were flinching. His hands, dry and ashy, were linked in front of him. Grey colored his hair and the stubble on his face, and his eyes were pink and tired.

But what saddened me most was his voice. He was a man who laughed like a hyena, a high-pitched eruption that was infectious. He was a man who talked with gusto and arrogance. This was why people were attracted to him, why my mother fell hard in 1973, why I thought he was legend.

In the restaurant, however, it was his breathing that was loud and wheezy, and his voice soft and raspy.

He told me about his heart again. For the first ten minutes, as we waited for our food, it was all he could talk about. My heart. My heart. My heart. His words were in an endless loop. He said he could be on disability, disability, if he allowed them to cut him open, cut him open, and examine him. He lived off severance pay, but that would end in January.

"My heart," he said.

"Cut open," he said.

When he paused, his eyes drifting off, I told him he should do it. I told him some money was better than no money. I told him he could know for sure what was wrong.

"I know already," he said.

"How?"

"Something is not right."

"No one is going to give you money on a hunch."

"If they open me, I will die. This for sure."

He had sought the advice of Buddha, praying for eight hours, and then he consulted his fortune-telling grids. He even went to see a palm reader who said there was a block in his heart line. Everything pointed to his demise if he allowed them to open his chest.

I didn't know what else to say, so when the food came, I ate. My father hardly touched his crispy-skinned pork, fat glistening. Instead, he watched me, smiling.

When I was done, he asked if I wanted more. Yes, I told him quickly, surprised at my response. I ordered wonton soup with egg noodles. I ordered crispy spring rolls.

The self, at times, can be fractured. It was one of the few lines I retained from my psychology class. This was another: The mind has the capacity for storing conflicting ideas. We love and hate, sometimes concurrently.

I had spent so much energy hating my father for the last two years that I didn't realize how much I missed him.

With a mouthful of noodles, I began to cry. I despised that I was crying. Tears dripped into broth. I did not stop eating. I shoveled noodles into my mouth. I crunched on the spring rolls. I did not look up. I felt my father's stare, and I knew he didn't know how to comfort me, his eighteen-year-old son who dwarfed him in size; he never did. That fact, however, was a comfort in itself. In the rapid changes in our lives, this remained constant.

I wiped my mouth and face.

"You remember," he said, "my story about the crazy dog?"

I nodded.

"You remember," he said, "how you wanted me to tell you those stories?"

I nodded.

"That dog," he said, "bit hard." He bent down to roll up his slacks. "You see?"

I nodded, but didn't look. I knew they were there, those missing chunks of him.

"You always wanted that story," he said.

I looked down at my empty bowl.

"That crazy dog took pieces of me."

ev

Imagine this wild boy in this wild land of snakes and piranhas and wild dogs. Imagine this wild boy whose knees are scraped and dirty, whose hands are as dusty as the roads. This boy, this wild boy, spends his time in the heat, swims in brown rivers, eats stolen fruit from neighboring trees. His energy is that of the monkeys that swing from branch to branch, a state of constant movement. You could see the boy dangling from the tallest trees. You could see him as the class clown, the one who is unafraid of the teacher's ruler, unafraid of anything, even fire ants, whose bite leaves tiny red dots, burning pin pricks. This wild boy sleeps outside, without netting, because the mosquitoes dislike the taste of his blood. He sleeps outside because, at times, he sleepwalks and wanders to dark open places. Inside, he breaks things. Bumps into walls. Wakes his mother. Angers his older sister. Outside, there is less danger.

Imagine this wild boy one night sleepwalking. He is barefoot, always barefoot, and the sharp rocks do not wake him. He walks with purpose. He walks as if someone awake.

Imagine this wild boy who steps on a dog. Imagine how suddenly he is awake. In one sleeping moment, he is dreaming of running faster than any boy in the universe, dreaming of being a streak, a blur, and then the next, waking to a dog clamped on his leg, and seeing blood spilling out, dark, a river of ink, and the sudden pain that shoots throughout the body. Imagine the scream. Imagine the swift kick the boy delivers to the dog. Imagine the sound of the dog scampering away. Imagine the wild boy on the dusty road, as dusty as his hands.

 భ

What my father never disclosed in the telling of his story is what happened to the boy afterwards. There were scars, of course, but who was it that cleaned his wounds? Who was it that told him how strong and brave he was to endure a vicious bite?

What my father never disclosed in the telling of his story is what happened with the dog. Younger, I didn't care. It was the boy I was amazed by. The boy who was far from being me. Living a Tom Sawyer life. Unafraid of anything.

Now, it is the dog I feel for most. It is the dog I worry over. It is the dog I want rescued from the sleepwalking boy.

What my father never disclosed is whether this story is true. I never questioned him, amazed at his ability to tell a story, the ebb and flow of his voice, how he strung along tension. Plus, why would he lie?

As a child, I swallowed everything my father said. I thought for so long that he was the example of an ideal man. I molded myself into that image, that exterior that is pumped with confidence and pride. This was all he allowed me to see. Underneath that was so much I didn't know. One thing is for sure: I know my father likes to spin tales until they become his mythology.

෬

The next several weeks, he would pick me up and we would head to the same restaurant. The cooks knew who we were and always treated us to larger servings. The waitress knew us, too, knew I took my cola with no ice, knew I always started with duck and rice, knew my father always ordered the crispy pig and sometimes stewed chicken feet, knew there was a possibility I would order another bowl of soup. Once she asked if we were father and son, and for a second I heard my father's old laugh and voice. "Yes," he said, loud enough for the entire restaurant to hear. "My son."

Each week, he came with a gift—always Fila T-shirts—and I started wearing them everywhere I went.

After the first week, I never thought of these visits as an inconvenience, as I did everything else that took me away from my friends and my moments to smoke. In fact, I saw my father more in our few hours together than my mother, who was constantly there. Always, when I returned home, she would be waiting at the front window. She asked the same questions.

"Have good time?"

"Yep."

"He asking for money?"

"Nope."

"He give you money?"

"Nope."

"He give you another shirt?"

"Yep?"

"Funny man."

One day, I found one of my father's T-shirts turned pink. My mother did my laundry and put them back in my drawers, and here was this pink T-shirt with an American flag on it and a tennis ball. Other items turned pink, also, some socks, a dress shirt I wore to work, but the T-shirt was what sent me into a fury.

I don't remember exactly what I said. I might have shaken the T-shirt in a clenched fist. I might have called my mother stupid or careless. I might have accused her of doing this on purpose. I might have yelled like a mad man. I might have cussed in English and in Thai.

Such outbursts, usually, would have enraged my mother. She would have matched my ferocity, her voice shaking the floors. But I remember how eerily calm she was. She looked at me and said, "I am sorry."

Well before the divorce, before any of this began, I remember being woken up by my father's booming voice like thunder in the night. I was, perhaps, ten or eleven, and I opened my bedroom door to see my father holding himself up over the bathroom sink, the door wide open, and my mother sitting on the lid of the toilet. Both his arms were on either side of the sink and they were pulsating. He shook, unaware I was watching him. His eyes remained on the drain. "Where is the fuckin' toothpaste?" he said in Thai. "I come home and there is no fuckin' toothpaste." He grabbed his brush and whipped it against the sink. "I want toothpaste." His voice was so loud, so deep, I did not recognize it at all.

In my entire life, I had never seen my father in this state. I couldn't move.

My mother rushed to close the bathroom door. I heard her say, "Mah bah." Rabid dog.

I don't remember much more of that night, only that the next day we got into a car and drove to a mansion in Glencoe to see this special doctor. My father was close friends with the owner of the house; he told the man's fortune weekly, instructing him to open more Thai restaurants in Chicago and invest money in gas stations. That weekend, the man housed this special doctor from Thailand who didn't look like a doctor, but an overweight construction worker. He was about sixty, his skin the color of a recently oiled baseball mitt. The adults went into one room, and I played Nintendo in another. When the owner's seven-year-old daughter came rushing in to tell me my father was crying, I darted down the hall to see my father's back shivering, hunched over, a deep muffled moan coming from his mouth. The doctor above him spoke a tongue I didn't understand. The other adults in the room prayed, their eyes snapped shut, except my mother who did not remove her gaze from my father. Her hands were in front of her, but her lips did not move.

Then suddenly, my father stilled. The prayers stopped. My mother made a move towards him, but caught herself. My father straightened. All I saw was the back of him, his pink dress shirt that was untucked from his brown slacks. I wanted to run to him, to see for myself his tear-streaked face, to ask him what was wrong.

The doctor asked how my father felt. His hands were on top of my father's shoulders, as if ready to push him down if needed.

I heard a deep breath. Then: "Better. Back to normal."

I didn't know what that meant. I still don't. When I watched *The Exorcist* a couple of years later at a friend's house, I remembered that night. When my mother railed against my father during their arguments, screaming at the top of her lungs, calling him Mah bah, accusing him of humping another woman like a dog, I remembered that night again. Not because my father met my mother's anger with his own, but because he remained still and calm—like my mother apologizing for the pink shirt. And I wondered what part of him was chased away in that mansion in Glencoe.

Maybe nothing.

Maybe the truth was he had already let go, like my mother had the day I went at her for destroying my T-shirt, and the only person still holding on, still hoping, was me.

೧

Mid-August and in a week I was returning to college. My father, before our next visit, had requested I bring pictures of myself. Baby pictures, pictures from high school, anything. When he picked me up, we didn't go to our usual restaurant, but only a block down to the McDonald's. I laughed. Told him I could've walked. He told me he had something to tell me.

"I'm going back to Thailand," he said.

I didn't answer him. I scanned the McDonald's, hoping no one I knew was here.

"It's too much to live here." I understood what he meant. Understood that soon he would have no income. He made a little by telling fortunes, but not enough to live in a city like Chicago.

"What are your plans?" I said.

He told me a string of things: real estate agent, golf pro, opening up a spa. Living in America had taught him how to survive. In Thailand, he'd be rich.

"When are you leaving?"

"Two weeks."

I nodded.

"When you come to Thailand, you stay with me. I will have a big house."

I nodded.

"I will call you when I get there."

I placed the bag of pictures in front of him. I had sorted through a few albums and selected about twenty pictures. My mother couldn't part with some of them, which made narrowing down difficult. What I had chosen was an eclectic mix: ones of me, ones of us, ones with my mother.

He went through them, smiling, remembering. He laughed at a few. He asked where some were taken. When he bumped into photos of my mother, he paused.

"Will she forgive me?"

I shrugged. "Probably not."

He looked at me. I knew what he wanted to say. Will you forgive me?

"Do you want a fish filet?" he said.

I smiled and rose out of the seat. "No thanks."

"Here," he said and threw me another T-shirt. "Present."

"Thanks." I swung the shirt over my shoulder and gave a quick wave before leaving. How long he would sit there I did not know. I imagined him ordering a fish filet and fries. I imagined him sipping his cola. I imagined him going through the pictures again. I imagined him wondering about all the decisions in his life and what had led him here, to this moment, and whether it was worth it.

But I don't think he did.

❧

We should never dwell on the past, Buddha said, never dream of the future; our minds should be fixed on the present moment. I wonder if Buddha got most of his teachings from a dog.

❧

Imagine this wild dog. Imagine this wild dog watching a sleep-walking boy. The dog's ears perk up. He is hoping the boy heads in another direction. It does not. During the day, this dog will scamper away from children, especially boys who like to tie things on him, who like to hit him with a stick. This is night, however, and boys are supposed to sleep. What this dog doesn't know is this boy is sleeping. What this dog doesn't know is this boy is only following a dream. The dog emits a low warning growl. The boy does not hear. The dog barks once. The boy does not hear. The dog does not want it to come to a bite. The dog only wants quiet. The dog only wants to rest his eyes before the hot sun rises again. He sees the sleepwalking boy's foot. He sees that its destination is his head. What is a wild dog to do?

ex

In *The Hidden Life of Dogs*, Elizabeth Marshall Thomas calculated that her Siberian Husky Misha, an escape artist, roamed a home territory of 130 square miles. Misha navigated Cambridge streets and traffic with ease. Along the way he made friends and enemies. Despite his adventures, he always came back, always knew where home was.

I'm not sure my father knows where home is. I'm not sure he is looking for home. He has traveled great miles, and the miles he put behind are behind him. He is never one to look back. At times, I admire this inner calling that sends him in so many directions at once. At times, I want to still him. I want to tell him that he will regret what he leaves behind. Part of me knows he does. Part of me recognizes that he hurts when he leaves. Part of me understands that he must go.

On walks with my dogs, it is easy to right the ship. I allow them to sniff and follow whatever entices them. I stop often, let them enjoy what their noses tell them, stories by smell, the past unraveling through the nasal passages. With an easy tug and a call of their names, they always come back. They are always by my side when I turn towards home.

Noisy Neighbor

In college, when most eighteen-year-olds discover a passion for bass-thumping woofers, three-a.m.-tripped fire-alarms, and, of course, gratuitous sighs of neighbors busily making love, I realized that I couldn't tolerate noise. I wasn't a prude, but I expected my neighbors to have the common courtesy to shut off their radios at night, to use what my second grade teacher referred to as "our six-inch voices."

When I lived with my roommate, in southern Illinois, our neighbors would wander in drunk at three in the morning, blast some bass-pumping music, and pass out. Meanwhile, our walls shook. The floor shook. Our belongings toppled over from the seismic energy. It would have been easy to walk over and knock on their door and tell them to turn it down. Instead, I waited, my muscles tight, for the moment my roommate would jump out of the bed and rage. He cussed, spit flying everywhere. And then the bare-knuckled punches on a wooden door or cement wall. Yes, the noise did bother me, but it was the waiting for the freak-out that was worse.

A year under those conditions made me a light sleeper. I became a person who waited for sound.

The apartment complex was comprised of several two-floor buildings. Each building had a total of eight units. The walls were thin, of course, and I heard conversations about the hottie in 7D or the unfair political science professor who thought he was in Harvard and not Saluki country where expectations were a little lower. One of my first neighbors, a sandy haired blonde guy named Keith—I accidentally got his mail once—had a new girl-friend. Keith was the type of guy with the gas-guzzling SUV that took up two parking spots; the type of guy that when his friends were over for beers he played hardcore rap, but when he was alone, he preferred the soothing ballads of Air Supply or Chicago; the type of guy who dated girls with names like Brandi or Tammi or Candi, all spelled with an "i."

Keith had acquired a new girlfriend, Misti probably, and it didn't take long before they became connected in the biological sense. For a month, like clockwork, they had sex at least once a day. They preferred doing it before dinner, which was my dinner time, and though I was entertained by the cornucopia of sounds, like porn on the radio, it made me bitterly aware that I was single.

Through the wall, I felt like I knew Keith, even though we didn't say a word to one another. He was from Peoria and worked in the mall part-time. He sang Madonna tunes in a beautiful fal-setto voice. In the parking lot, if we bumped into each other, we nodded.

Sex came earlier one day, but something wasn't right. Keith's sounds I knew. He was a series of grunts, short burst of breaths, and at climax, a long throaty note of satisfaction. His partner usu-ally sounded like a high-pitched hyper-ventilator, like she was not getting enough air and her breath was cut short. I thought, on several occasions, she was going to pass out from coital delight.

Keith's partner that day was not his girlfriend.

This one was a hummer, a giggler, a gasper. She was a talker, too, but not hot sex talk, but casual conversation talk, like, "When we're done (gasp) maybe we can (giggle) go to Applebee's (hum) for Happy Hour."

Can I come too? I wanted to say. I love the Bourbon Street Steak.

The sex didn't last long and they didn't go to Applebee's afterwards. All I heard was Keith weeping, and saying he had fucked up. I warmed up a frozen Lean Cuisine entrée in the microwave and huddled against the wall for story time.

໙

Misti was not forgiving, and neither, it seemed, was the temptress. Poor Keith eventually moved out. This was the nature of living in this apartment complex. My neighbors came and went. Some graduated, some flunked out. Some were forcibly removed by the landlord for illegal substances on the premises—the smell of weed wafting from underneath apartment doors—or vomiting in the pool or drunk and disorderly conduct. Keith was replaced by an Indian student who, in the afternoons, blared Bollywood music for the bewildered Illinoisans to hear. He lasted a semester and was replaced by a frazzled-looking woman with big bulky glasses. She knocked many times on my door, asking to borrow computer paper, looking as if she were on the verge of a breakdown. She talked to herself often, and I always heard the buzz of her printer. A philosophy major.

And finally: the woman with the dog.

໙

I only knew of my new neighbor because of the barking. The first week was intolerable. The dog barked at my every sound. If I walked to the kitchen and the floor creaked, it barked. If I used the bathroom, it barked. Throughout the day, I sat as still as possible, not moving an inch in fear of the bark. The dog seemed constantly aware of me, directing its bark as I moved through my apartment. I barely had enough sleep because I stayed up late into the night, not because of the bark, but because of the prospects of the bark. I learned to anticipate every canine tremble. During the day, I tried to cover it up with music, turning the volume high so all I could hear was the hard alternative stuff I was currently into, but the bark penetrated the chaos of drums and screechy electric guitar solos.

I'd been reading poetry for my literature course, learning the rhythms of verse, and the barks were like alarming end stop lines to an unwritten poem of a single man's life. In Billy Collins's poem, "Another Reason I Don't Keep a Gun in the House," he writes about the neighbor dog's endless bark.

> I close all the windows in the house
> and put on a Beethoven symphony full blast
> but I can still hear him muffled under the music,
> barking, barking, barking,
> and now I can see him sitting in the orchestra,
> his head raised confidently as if Beethoven
> had included a part for barking dog.

This bark was not just part of the music. It was part of every sound of the day.

I thought I would go mad. I even considered wooing my room-mate back, so he could rage and possibly terrify the dog into si-lence. I thought if the barking didn't stop I would march over to the main office with my complaint.

I had it all planned out. Something melodramatic. When you live alone, you let your imagination run. I would take my cue from Tom Cruise in *A Few Good Men*. I would express my discontent with a bulging vein in my forehead. I would tell the landlord in a slick and coy and cocksure voice, "Miss Landlady, I have been paying good goddamn money"—I would say goddamn—"for over a year. Never late with the rent. Never a complaint about me." I paused to allow for that serious silence to settle. The landlord re-coiled in her cheap office chair. She watched me with a frightened eye, watched how I knotted my jaw. Then I said, "Now tell me, what are we gonna do about that goddamn dog?"

I didn't follow through.

Not just because it was never in me to do something like that, but because I received a note from my new neighbor. It was on a light blue index card. It smelled nice. *Sorry for all the barking*, it read. *She's a pup. We're in training. She'll be quieter. I promise.*

❧

Living on your own you fall into a routine. You wake up at the exact same time every day, 7:35 a.m. You eat the same breakfast, a banana and vitamin supplements, and counteract it all with two-and-a-half cigarettes on the drive to school. You park in the same spot, cross the same railroad tracks, and get to your class about ten minutes early so you can smoke. After classes, you find a coffee-house off the strip and sip on a cappuccino, reading. Sometimes a friend joins you and you gossip about the hot new English lit professor from NYC or whether the hippie with endless hair is sleeping with that malnourished nerd who talks about literature in another language. But often you are alone with Virginia Woolf or Thomas Hardy or Jane Austen. Finishing your mid-afternoon break, you head to the gym, run on the treadmill, lift minimal weights, play an hour of tennis with a pro who is half the size of you but can hit the ball a ton. When you're done, you think about your options for dinner: 1) frozen entrée, 2) chicken wings and fried rice from the Chinese place, 3) cook something. It's usually option one or two, unless it's a weekend, and you make the one recipe you mother has taught you, Thai chicken in the oven.

The dog had worked itself into my routine. When I climbed the stairs into my apartment, it would start to bark. The bark had changed in the last three weeks. No longer was it high-pitched and projected as if through a megaphone. It was calmer, less alarming, more like a greeting. No longer did it bark when I moved about. Instead, I listened to its collar jiggling as it trotted from place to place, and it was like the small temple bells in Thailand, a sound that immediately soothed me.

I had not seen the dog, not once, but I knew the owner had her own routines. In the morning, up even before me, she took the dog out for a run, returning just as I began peeling my banana. She watched *Friends* and *ER* regularly—I heard Dr. Green question a diagnosis often—and Sarah McLachlan sang softly through her CD player at night. Like me, her mother called every day at the same time, but unlike me, she spent more than a few seconds talking to her. In the evening, around seven or eight, she took the dog out again. I sometimes hurried to the peephole to catch a glimpse of the dog, but it was too small to see. I only heard its clicky claws on the linoleum floors, and usually caught a glimpse of my neighbor, a streak of brown hair whizzing by.

As much as I was fascinated with the dog, I was as fascinated with its faceless owner. Sometimes I heard her through the wall. When the dog barked at an alien sound, she was quick to silence it with a delicate voice. *Hush now. Everything is OK. It was just the wind.* Her voice was like a gentle wind, and it immediately calmed the dog. Hearing it I imagined the kindest woman in the world; there was a princess-like etherealness to her voice, as if she was out to charm anyone in her proximity.

I began to imagine what she might look like. Her skin was white, so white that on winter days, only her cheeks and the tip of her cute nose turned pink. Her eyes were light blue, the same blue of the index card she left me, and she possessed long swirly hair like ripples in water. She wasn't skinny like CK models, but athletic, sturdy, what The Commodores called a "Brick house." I imagined she enjoyed ripped jeans and T-shirts and bandanas, and didn't mind putting her hair into pigtails. She had a laissez-faire attitude about appearance, never wearing make-up, but who needed it when you had lips and cheeks as red as a cherry.

My imaginations went far beyond appearance. I went on dates with her: romantic dog walks in wide open meadows or horseback riding even though I was petrified of horses or classic English balls. She was accompanied by her dog. I was reading too much Austen and all I could think about was Darcy's home in Pemberley and the scenic expanse of the Lake District. How odd would it have been to have an Asian man like me from Chicago wooing an elegant English woman in the early 1800s? No matter. Our love defied social boundaries. Who in their right mind would stop something so beautiful?

"Dude, you need to get the fuck out of the apartment."

My friends from Chicago called often at night, especially Derek, my overly testosteroned Polish pal who worked in the lumber section at Home Depot. Though he was the crassest person I'd ever met, there was a sensitive side to him, a romantic comedy side he never showed anyone but me. Because of this, I told Derek about the neighbor and her dog and my strange imaginings.

"She could be the one," I said. "You ever think of that?"

"You haven't met her."

"I have a feeling. More than a feeling." I went on to sing a couple bars of Boston's hit song, off tune and obnoxious, then thought whether the woman heard my pitchy voice through the wall.

"Shut up," Derek said, though I could hear him laughing. "For real, go knock on her door. Don't be such a pussy."

"You knock on her door."

"You know I would. I'd be hitting that shit sideways and the dog could be licking my balls."

"Appropriate."

"Don't get college on me."

The dog barked once, and I thought it knew what Derek had said and was not happy.

"Listen," Derek said. "Three things. One, you need to get the fuck out of that apartment. Stop reading those cheesy books you got. Two, go over there and say hi. That's it. If she's the one, you'll know for sure. Three, I got a surprise for you. Should be arriving next week. You'll love it." He laughed and hung up.

Fuck.

ço

In my Literature Appreciation class, taught by a graduate student whose name has slipped through the cracks of my memory, we read Chekhov's "The Lady with the Dog." Most of the discussion centered on Chekhov's style. "In many ways," the TA said, "he is the father of minimalism. He paved the way for Hemingway and Carver." We examined closely the power of simplicity, how the smallest number of words created maximum effect. I enjoyed this class, enjoyed my teacher's enthusiasm. He was one of those cool teachers with a goatee, spiked hair, and round wire-rimmed glasses. He spoke animatedly with his hands and either sat on the desk or flipped the chair around and straddled it. During the entire semester, I never saw him wear anything else but a suede patched sports coat and dress shirt. Often, we smoked together on the English building balcony.

"This is a blueprint, people, to the short story form as it is today."

He opened it up for further discussion. One of the stupider ones in class said, "I hated the title. It's called 'The Lady with the Dog,' or whatever, and the dog was barely in there. It could've been called 'The Lady.'" He nodded like he had said something profound. "Like, I don't even remember what kind of dog it was."

I rolled my eyes. Pomeranian, moron, I wanted to say. I sat in the back, an observer, not much into participation yet. I was between majors and wasn't sure I would commit to English.

The TA caught me. "You look like you want to say something."

I shrugged.

"Come on," he said.

"Well, the dog was the reason Dmitri and Anna met," I said quietly. "He paid attention to the dog. It was a Pomeranian. Without the dog, you wouldn't have the affair. You wouldn't have a story." I felt semi-profound saying this, but I remembered I didn't have a clue about the breed of my neighbor's dog, the one I almost lived with. And despite our weeks together, I never heard its name.

I don't remember what happened in class after that. I don't remember much except for all the books and poems and stories we read in that class. That I could never forget. Afterwards, however, on the smoker's balcony, my mind rounded back to the story. Two unhappy people stuck in unhappy marriages. Chekhov's story made me feel lonely all of a sudden. I puffed on a cigarette, my eighth one of the day, on schedule. I thought about having another one when my TA came out, an unlit cigarette already between his lips. He nodded at me, lit his stick, and said, "Thank you for not being stupid."

✺

On my door was a UPS delivery slip. A package for me was left with my neighbor. I shuddered. This was Derek's plan all along. To make me knock on her door. To set eyes on her for the first time. To introduce myself.

I went into my apartment and hopped into the shower. When I was done, I coated myself with cologne, the good stuff. Putting on a sweater vest and jeans, I went over what I would say and how I would say it. Should I be like Fonzi, and act like I was too-cool-for-school? Should I be like James Dean, tortured and magnetic? Or how about cocky like Cary Grant? Before I could step out of my apartment, I heard her door open and the dog's speedy trot. When I opened my door, they were gone, but a box was on the ground. I picked it up. I knew what was in it immediately. Porn. Derek's favorite. It was addressed to Penis Head, and it was from the man who loves you the most.

☙

In late spring, my mother called and said she wanted to spend the weekend with me. She would take the train and get in Friday evening. She hadn't seen the apartment since she moved me in. I wanted to impress her; her only son was now an adult. I ditched Friday classes to clean the house and hide all of Derek's porn. He was relentless. After the videos came magazines and then a porn CD-rom. Every package was addressed to Penis Head, or sometimes Mr. Penis Head.

I tore down my posters of scantily clad women and replaced them with posters of my favorite tennis players. I dusted off my Buddha in my bedroom and sprayed the apartment with air freshener, hoping it would mask the stale smoke scent. I cleaned out the refrigerator, a gruesome task, and made sure to stock it with vegetables. That weekend, I planned to cook for my mother for the first time.

When she arrived, this adult persona I had planned to assume melted away. We reverted back to our roles. I was her son. She was my mother. We were comfortable with that.

In general, my mother was low maintenance. She didn't need to go out. She liked sitting on the balcony of my apartment looking at the world and reading her Thai soap opera magazines. In the evenings, if there was a horror movie or animal documentary on television, she was content. I drove her to campus Saturday afternoon and I gave her a tour of all the buildings I had classes in. The hardest part of her visit was I couldn't smoke. This remained a secret.

On the Sunday before she left, I cooked her dinner. I was clumsy with the knife, careless with my measurements. In truth, I was nervous and kept saying this was no way like Thai chicken in Thailand. The end result: the chicken was burnt and overly salted; the rice was too wet. My mother, however, ate without complaint. She said I was becoming a man. I told her to be quiet, but felt good inside.

When we were done, we sat at the dining table. I could hear the dog scratching itself on the other side of the wall. I imagined how confusing this weekend was for it. Suddenly there was a new alien voice next door to bark at. And this voice did not speak an understandable language. This voice sometimes laughed too loudly when an ax murderer killed a teenager on TV. This voice liked to sing the soundtrack to *The Sound of Music*, mispronouncing the lyrics.

"I don't want to leave," my mother said in Thai.

"Stay the week. I'll cook every day"

She smiled and shook her head. "Work."

"Call in sick," I suggested, but knew my mother would never do it. After working over thirty years as a nurse she had probably accrued enough sick days to last five years, yet, in my entire life, she never took a day off, even on those hard days during the divorce, when all her emotional energy was zapped out of her.

"I'd like to come more often," she said. "Peaceful here."

"I always need my laundry done."

She smacked my hand. "Lazy," then, "Better find a good wife to do all this work."

"Whatever."

"Thai wife."

"Whatever."

"Not like the pictures I find in your closet."

I nearly choked. She found my posters—blondes, brunettes, redheads in wet T-shirts.

She began to laugh, covering her mouth with her hand. I hadn't seen her laugh this hard in a long time.

The dog barked, and she laughed harder, hitting the table.

In the middle of the night, I woke up to mother singing softly to herself and the dog barking. She was usually up at this hour, working the night shift. Underneath the crack of my bedroom door, the light was on and I assumed she was reading. When she found a break in the song, she told the dog, "Good boy, good girl, good boy, good girl," in a sing-song whisper. It didn't take long. The dog stopped barking, and I fell back asleep.

తి

In Dr. Ian Dunbar's book *How To Teach a New Dog Old Tricks*, he writes: "No one would think of putting a shock collar on a canary, squirting lemon juice into a baby's mouth or beating a husband with a rolled-up newspaper and having his vocal cords cut out for 'singing' in the shower. However, people think nothing of doing all of these and more to barking dogs."

I won't lie. In that first week, any of these options seemed viable. But the barking became part of my day. It was something I learned to adjust to. In fact, I grew to love the sound of it.

One afternoon, I decided to do some studying at the library. I shut my door but left my keys inside the apartment. I tried to break in with a credit card, something I had always been gifted at, but the lock wasn't friendly. I had no way of getting a hold of maintenance, and the main office was closed on Sundays.

I decided to finally do it. I knocked on my neighbor's door.

The dog went into an excited fit of barking, as if it too had been waiting for this moment. I heard it leaping on the door, its little paws pushing off the wood. Then I heard her voice. *Hush*, she said. *Quiet, baby.* When she opened up, the dog rushed out and started barking and sniffing. It went back and forth between my legs; it hopped up and pushed off my thighs.

"He doesn't bite," she said.

I knelt down and let him sniff my hand. "I locked myself out," I said, more to the dog than her. The dog was black and tan with a clipped tail. He moved his body against my hands, wiggling and sniffing and barking. I stood up. When I did, he backed away and barked again.

"Mind if I use your phone to call maintenance?"

Finally, I took a good look at her. She was beautiful, but not the way I had imagined her. She did not have brown hair at all, but blonde and short. She wore glasses that she pushed up her nose, giving her that cute nerdy appearance.

"Sure," she said. "Come in."

I was happy to see that her place was as nondescript as mine, minus the busty babes posters. It smelled nicer for sure, and I noticed a bowl of potpourri on top of her TV. Her couch was blue, while mine was a pink with swirly designs that made it look camouflage. She pointed to a phone. It resembled keys on a piano.

"Do you have the number?" I said.

"Yeah," she said and disappeared into the bedroom. The dog stayed with me. I was mesmerized by his movements, how he curled into a C around my legs. He kept barking and barking. Wiggling and wiggling. He appeared to be saying, At last! At last!

She came out with a sheet of phone numbers management gave us when we moved in. "He likes you," she said.

"I like him." I dialed, and as the phone rang, I asked her what kind of dog he was.

"Cocker spaniel."

"He's adorable."

The maintenance guy picked up. I told him I was locked out. I told him my apartment number. He said he'd be over in ten minutes.

I gave her back the sheet of phone numbers. "Thanks a lot."

"No problem," she said.

"I like your phone."

"Silly, isn't it?"

"Pretty cool actually."

"Does his barking ever bother you?"

The dog was sitting now, looking up at me, his tongue hanging out the side of his mouth. I knelt down again and offered him my hand. He came and licked it twice and forced his way closer. I patted him all over. "I don't even notice it."

We didn't see much of each other after that. Sometimes I'd pass the two of them on the stairs and we'd say hi, the dog always happy to see me. After our meeting, he didn't bark as much. Why would he when he knew the person on the other side of the wall?

Derek was right. I would know if she was the one if I knocked on her door. She wasn't. Who would believe in such silly notion anyway? I had. A boy who lived alone in an apartment. A boy sensitive to sound.

In *Pride and Prejudice*, which we covered not long before Chekhov, Darcy spoke too rashly to his friend about Elizabeth Bennet. "She is tolerable; but not handsome enough to tempt me." Darcy and Elizabeth took hundreds of pages to realize they were in love and within those hundreds of pages they were understanding themselves before they could understand each other.

All I understood of that day was, yes, my Illinois neighbor was beautiful, and yes, she had a cool piano phone, and yes, her apartment smelled like flowers, but it was her dog I found of interest, and it was his voice that for months was my companion on lonely nights.

My Dog Ginger

. . . wonders why the Thai woman visiting her house speaks in a language she does not understand. When the Thai woman says I love you, my dog Ginger tilts her head, and when the Thai woman says good girl, my dog Ginger barks. Even a Thai woman understands the meaning of a bark.

My dog Ginger does not know the woman is Thai, only that she is short and smells like an attic full of moth balls and vapor rub. When the Thai woman arrives she sets down baskets of stinky food in easy grab-and-go height—which my dog Ginger likes—but the Thai woman smothers her in her arms—which my dog Ginger most definitely does not. She also knows that the Thai woman moves first before looking, and that she should always be on the watch for a cheap sneaker heading in the direction of her sleeping head.

In the early morning, however, when the Thai woman sits on the easy chair, a cup of instant coffee steaming on the windowsill, losing herself to the goldfinches at the feeders and the downy woodpecker ambling up the river birch, my dog Ginger creeps up a little closer, sometimes jumping onto her lap, and the both of them watch the day rise.

She will grow to like the Thai woman despite her foreignness, despite her awkward way of patting her head, which is more like kneading dough. She will even like how the Thai woman says her name, the sound of summer crickets.

When the Thai woman leaves, she, like her master, will wait by the guestroom door for the next few weeks, wondering when the Thai woman will come out and suffocate them both with her unrelenting love.

II.

Mr. Mouth

On Trenton Doyle Hancock's Self-Portraits
or Two FAT Men Meet and Bump Bellies
or Shut Up! I'm Eating

Mr. Mouth

You eat. That's what you do. When asked what your occupation is, you do not say writer or artist. You do not say educator. You say, I am a professional eater. You say I am in the business of devouring. Sometimes you don't know what goes in; most of the time you don't. A professional eater is a not a food critic. He does not analyze food. He does not register taste. He is continuous action. He is mouth without thought. A professional eater is akin to the professional athlete. Eating is simply the movement of the jaw, the act of consuming, of shoveling in. The mouth is strangely elastic. Open it as wide as you can. Feel the strain at the corners. Feel the jaw at the point of unhinging.

Have you seen the skinny Japanese put away hot dogs on the Fourth of July? Or the Youtube video of the man shoving ping-pong ball after ping-pong ball into his mouth? It does not matter what clings to your facial hair, what pokes and prods at your bulbous cheeks. In the end, the mouth can devour anything and everything.

Buff and Britches

Buff and Britches

We dissect the body. We do this with ease. Go ask a stranger what they love about their body, and they will give you a story.

We say, I love my legs.

We say, Look at how toned my arms are.

I used to have a friend who walked around school flexing his forearms. A thick vein meandered down to his elbow. Check this shit out, he'd say and then flex like he was Mr. Universe. We are endless with parts we love and don't love.

We cleave the body. Dissect it with surgical precision. Denigrate them into Pro and Con piles. Parts everywhere. Lips, eyes, chin. Fingers, toes. Breasts, chests, ass.

But what if—what if everything is a con? What if there is nothing you like about yourself? What if you have been so critical about your body, scrutinized under your personal microscope, so critical of your life, that there is nothing to like at all? Not one hair. Not one toenail.

Then you become without shape. Then you become unmolded clay. Then you cease to have function. Body is nothing without its parts.

Sometimes We Can't Have the Things We Want

Sometimes We Can't Have the Things We Want

"I want." In Old Norse, want, or vante, means to lack. To want has been coded into our DNA. We are always found wanting. We are always found needing. When I was younger, I wanted and needed a lot of things. And because my Thai parents spoiled their only child rotten, I got what I wanted and needed. Want, however, can be misleading. Want can take us on the wrong path. I wanted my father's mini-van and got his mini-van before he left. What I really wanted was for him to stay.

Famous Wants by Famous People:

Einstein: "I want to know all God's thoughts."

Confucius: "I want to be everything that is you, deep at the center of your being."

Oscar Wilde: "I want my food dead."

Trent Doyle Hancock: "Fuck, I want that cheeseburger."

Ira Sukrungruang: "Me, too, Trent. It's beautiful in its pinkish glow."

Faster

Faster

It is aggravating—no?—the weight you carry. It is more than the weight of your physical self. It is the metaphorical weight, the fat that clogs the metaphorical heart, the fat that causes you to think in metaphors. As in: your fat is the undulating land of dips and plunges. As in: your fat is tumors clinging desperately to the bony frame. As in: fat is fat is fat.

So you join a gym. Heed Wallace Stevens' proclamation in one of his poems (you don't remember which), "Fat! Begone!" And you want fat to be gone. To be sucked up into the sky and cling to the yellow sun.

The gym is not filled with fat people. It is filled with lithe bodies. They are pixies compared to your bulk. You can eat two of them and they would fit comfortably in your living room stomach. And these pixies stare. You feel it. Wide eyes, as you get on the treadmill. And the treadmill stares too. And the treadmill says, You are FAT. And the treadmill says, I can't help you. And the treadmill says, Everyone is watching. You look forward. You increase your speed. You walk but get nowhere.

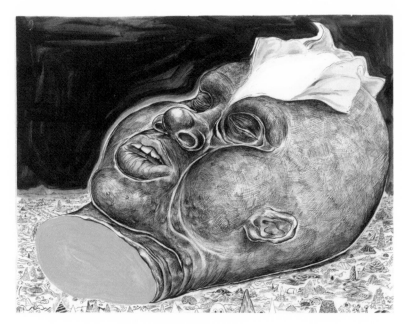

The Doorstop

The Doorstop

I've seen many doorstops in my life. Really strange ones. A halved bowling ball, for example. A Raggedy Anne doll wedged under the slit of a door. A little-league baseball trophy. Cement blocks stolen from the construction site across the street. A taxidermied beaver. My friend used to keep his door open with a mannequin's arm. He'd wedge the arm under the door, the hand and fingers waving on the other side. This I found most creepy because once I tripped over the hand during a drunken night, and thought zombies were coming out of the ground.

The hand, however, made me think of the body. And the body made me think of the head and the head made me think of baseball. Memory does this. It skips and jumps and lands on moments in our lives we have nearly forgotten. Like baseball with a mannequin's head. Like Tommy W stealing a head from a department store and us Chicago boys taking swings at it at the park. Everyone got a shot before it shattered. Split right down the middle. Someone said cool. Someone said whoa. We gathered around the head like we gathered around a nudie magazine. Only we were not gawking at naked bodies, but a broken head, bits of shattered plastic and molding. And there was knowledge in that cracked head. And we thought we were peering into a well of wisdom. And for one extended second, we said nothing because we saw power, because we saw the destructiveness of boys. And suddenly our own heads were open, though our eyes remained shut throughout it all.

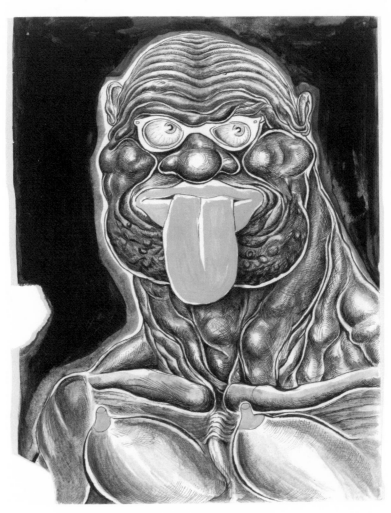

Self-Portrait with Tongue

Self-Portrait with Tongue

Let me tell you about an assignment some crazy fat creative writing teacher gave in his nonfiction class. He's fat because he's always saying he's fat, like how Fat Albert announces himself from miles away. He says on the first day of class, If you ever need to find me ask someone about the crazy fat Asian professor. There's only one of us around. He's crazy because he likes to talk with his hands and stuff. Sometimes his button is undone on his shirt and his belly button is exposed. He's crazy because he makes us do weird assignments. He stands up there with his hip rip-off Polo shirt and says: Write a self-portrait.

I say: How?

Crazy Teacher says: Go get inspired.

I say: How do I get inspired?

Teacher says: Think about yourself in a way you never thought about yourself.

I say: How do we think about ourselves in a way we never thought about ourselves?

Fat Teacher says: Try. And write.

I say: Are there examples of written self-portraits?

Crazy Fat Teacher says: Create your own example.

I say: Pretend you're us. How would you write yours?

Teacher says: Look at Trenton Doyle Hancock's "Self Portrait with Tongue." What do you see?

I say: A man with a tongue. And nipples.

Teacher says: What is the story?

I say: Is that what you want? A story?

Teacher says: I want what you want. I want you to dig. How do you view yourself? What image do you project? What image do you keep hiding? We are made of hundreds of versions of our-selves. Sometimes we are gluttonous globs. Sometimes we are the superhero atop a white tiger. Sometimes we are a desire and a rage. Sometimes we are buff. Sometimes we exist in a realm no one un-derstands. Excavate that.

I say: This isn't gonna be easy.

Teacher says: It's not meant to be.

III.

Thirteen Ways of Looking at Fat

I

There is, of course, the vantage of the reflection. He stares. He moves. He jiggles. He lifts his heft and lets it drop. Every motion occurs first in the brain. The hands that trace the hair. The toes that curl. The nostrils that flare. Remember: he is movement without thought. He only mimics. He knows nothing of the weight you carry, but knows only that he carries it.

II

Let me tell you about the three giggling girls. They wear Greek letters on their sweatshirts, but I don't think they know what they mean. I don't think they know much, except that the guy across the room, with the fashionable hair, is cute. They talk like sparrows.

This is a strange room we are in. No windows. Asylum white. A room from a nightmare.

The girls, they vary in size. One is small. One is medium. One is large. They talk, as if they occupy the same body, share the same thoughts. They talk about the guy across the room. He is the only one worth looking at.

Someone in class says, "It's OK to be fat."

The chirping stops. The small one makes a face. The medium one puffs a breath. The large one says, "But why would you want to be?"

The cute guy says nothing. He rests his head in his hands, and the glaze over his eyes suggests he is elsewhere. Outside, perhaps, where the sun is out and three sparrows are chirping high in a leafless tree.

III

I will not lie, Wallace, but you were fat. Not the fat that slows the heart and fattens the tongue, but the everyday man fat.

I found a photo.

You were sitting next to Frost and the two of you looked like the last thing you wanted to do was to be caught in a photo together. Frost looked like his poems, a moment of heightened realization, but there were shadows in his eyes and around the curls of his mouth. You, Wallace, were a man who did not look comfortable in his skin. You sat as if you were trying to conceal something. You did not know what to do with your hands. They were meaty and in your lap. They looked like hands meant to strangle. How those hands could write such delicate poems I do not know.

I read that you thought you were freakishly fat. You were diagnosed with acromegaly, a disorder that sounds as rotund as its definition: a condition causing progressive enlargement of the head, hands, and feet.

Of this I am sure—you and Frost would rather have mused about a leaf blowing in an autumn wind. Frost would have written about the life of the tree it came from, its branching ways. You would have just written that there was a leaf in an autumn wind and it was whirling.

IV

"I like the way it feels," my lover says. "There are so many soft spots."

There is one in particular she likes. Even I like to touch it. It is a rubbing stone, one you keep in your pocket and work away at until there's nothing but silkiness to its surface. That spot is south of the border, I like to say, where the stomach ends and the legs begin. The left side.

It is a secret canyon.

The light does not touch it.

It is left to the mind to fill in the necessary details.

"I can play with this all day," my lover says.

Times like this, my body and I are one. My lover and I, intertwined like this, are also one.

V

A multiple-choice question.

How many ways have you looked at yourself, Wallace?

VI

I have often imagined that there exists a shadow world. I overindulged in fantasy when younger. I do it now. On nightly walks—the moon or the city lights as my only source of illumination—I can't help but let my brain transport me to a place where trees dance without color, where the blackbird is at home and his flight is a streak racing across the lighted pavement.

There is this boy. He feels as if he rules the shadows. His body is not obtrusive. He glides along the walls, slips into the cracks in the sidewalk. He bleeds into other shadows, and has the power to manipulate the shapes of them. He likes to laugh, this boy, but what his mouth emits is the sound of silence.

There are words in the shadow world that have no meaning: hide, loathe, the variations of darkness. The boy does not know the meaning of fat. He lives in the world of mischief, and in the world of mischief, it helps to be blind to meaning. In shadow, when the boy eats, it appears as if he is eating himself.

VII

The thin man sees a fat man and says, "Boy, he is fat."
The fat man sees a fat man and says, "Boy, he is fat."

VIII

Please understand, from whatever angle you look at me, you will see something new. It is hard to keep this a secret. Through the eyes of a blackbird I am no different from anyone else. My movement—no matter how sluggish or slow—will cause flight.

I assure you, however, I am like you, Wallace, the common man. I sing your poems: Fat! Fat! Fat! Fat! I am the personal. Your world is you. I am my world.

IX

I venture further and further into the woods. I listen to the sounds—the breeze whistling through the leaves, the snapping branches under my feet, the twittering above me. In some fantasy worlds, trees can speak and move. They can uproot themselves and travel to a place where they face the sun.

When I was younger, I loved to wrap my arms around the trunks of trees, press my cheek against the bark. I tried to connect my fingers in the back, but never came close.

Now, my lover does the same. There is an immovable-ness about me.

In these woods, my girth is my trunk; my limbs are my branches. I stand still at the outer edge. I wait for the sun.

X

And remember: in this vast ocean, you will sink. Fat won't help you float. This is a myth. You will go straight to the bottom. Minnows will nibble the flesh peeling off your bones. They will make homes in your body. The belly button cave. The tubular innards.

You will not eat. You will be eaten.

My suggestion: if there is a green light above you, reach for it.

XI

I don't remember his name, but I remember his shape. He looked like a misshapen pear. His face was so fat he could barely talk; his voice was weighed down by the chubbiness of his cheeks. I enjoyed the fact that I had been demoted.

He was afraid, this boy, and his fear made him lash out. "Stop talking about me," he said to skinny-bones Mark P.

I watched him from the other side of the playground, near the swings.

Mark P. said nothing.

"I said stop talking about me," and before skinny Mark P. could do anything, the fat kid whose name I don't remember pushed him onto the ground.

I wondered if, when Mark looked up, he witnessed an eclipse. I wondered whether he thought a meteor was going to crash down on him.

It looked as if the fat kid whose name I don't remember was going to fly through the sky and crush poor Mark P. into the tar, into a fossil. But before any of that could happen, the lunch moms stopped it all.

A change came over the fat kid whose name I don't remember. He started to cry. "Tell him to stop talking about me. Tell them all to stop."

He was taken into the school. What happened after the incident has escaped my mind. I think he went to another school. Maybe he lost weight and became someone else.

But this is what I remember: When skinny Mark P. got up, he brushed himself off and said something under his breath. There was no mistaking the shape of one of the words.

XII

Wallace: You ten-foot poet among inchlings. Fat! Begone!

XIII

It was dinnertime all day.
It was snowing. All day it would be snowing.
Fat sat at the top of a cedar.
Its limbs were holding.

Fattest, Ugliest, Weirdest

When Paul Hutchkins transferred from whatever school he came from my freshman year, I was immediately dethroned as the fattest kid in school. Not that people kept lists of stuff like that—not in writing, anyway—but that was how I thought. Fattest. Toughest. Hottest. Weirdest. Ugliest. I was two hundred sixty pounds, and for most of my life, my friends had called me fat. Over time, however, it had become a term of endearment, they said, a way of saying, "Hey, Ira, what's up?"

This was not the case with Paul Hutchkins.

When he walked through the hallways of Oak Lawn Community High School, he was the fat that made people squish their faces in disgust. In the hallways of OLCHS, a few students actually fell to the ground clutching the wall, shouting, "Earthquake." When he walked through the hall, he was bombarded with insults: fatty, fat fuck, fatso. Tommy W, Craziest and Toughest, had the best nickname for Paul. Stay Puff, after the giant marshmallow monster in the movie *Ghostbusters*.

I took a liking to Paul for the same reason anyone takes a liking to another beneath his or her social status. I liked him because I wasn't him. Because now, there was a bigger person, a person who made loud breathing noises, a person whose eyes seemed closed because his cheeks looked like two pink saddlebags. Not only did Paul take over Fattest, but he was also top on the lists of Ugliest and Weirdest.

Almost predictably, Paul was a loner. At lunch he sat by himself and ate nothing. Not one bit. He stared out the cafeteria windows, past the football field, past school grounds. You could tell he was somewhere else, somewhere far from the school, and I wondered where that place was and what it looked like. Paul was also deep. I could tell that about him immediately. We had something in common. We both wanted more, but didn't quite know how to get it.

Perhaps because of his weight, Paul was also a narcoleptic. He fell asleep at random times, in weird places. He snored and it was loud and disruptive and made everyone laugh in class. Sometimes when the guys and I walked to school, we would find Paul sitting against the fence, sleeping.

"He's the ugliest motherfucker I have ever seen," Rob said one day in the early fall. "Just look at him. I want to puke." Rob started making upchuck noises over Paul. Paul didn't stir.

"Seriously," said Dan. "How could anybody be that fat?"

"Am I that fat?" I asked.

"Hell no," said Rob.

"Don't get us wrong," said Dan. "You're still a fatty. But this kid, he's two of you and that's a giant motherfucker."

"He's a joke," Rob said. Rob knelt down an inch from Paul's cheek. "He looks like bad cheese." He sniffed. "He smells like it, too."

"We're gonna be late," I said.

"Who cares?" said Rob. He opened his backpack and took out a marker. He wrote on Paul's face. "Fat" across the forehead. "Fat" on each of his cheeks. "Fat" on his chin. Paul didn't feel a thing. He continued to snore.

"Enough," I said. I kicked Paul's feet. I kicked his leg and said, "Hey, fatty. Get up. Hey, lard ass, you're going to be late for school."

Paul opened his eyes. He looked right at me. He mumbled something I couldn't understand.

"Get up," I said. "You're going to be late."

Rob and Dan started cracking up. They kept pointing at his face.

"Thanks," said Paul. It sounded like a gurgle. He rolled himself up, pulling at the fence, grunting.

"Whatever, Fatty," I said.

*

By the time he got to English I, Paul just had smudges on one of his cheeks. Mr. B paired students up for an interview assignment. We were supposed to make up a list of ten questions to ask each other. I was paired with Paul. I made a face and sighed.

Paul didn't sit in desk chairs like the rest of us. He sat at a large table where Mr. B spread out the papers he had left to grade. Sometimes Paul fell asleep in class and snored, and Mr. B would kick him awake. Mr. B had the reputation of being the coolest teacher in the school, ultra-suave, ultra fit, coach of the swimming team and in charge of student council, and Paul managed to get under his skin for doing absolutely nothing but sleep.

When the class started the interviews, the room burst into chatter. Paul and I didn't say anything but looked at each other. He stared right at me and I tried to hold his stare, but couldn't. I could still see the remains of the word "fat" on his face like a faded temporary tattoo.

"Why do people hate me?" Paul said. His voice was deep and throaty and slow.

"What?"

"You heard me," he said.

"I don't know," I said. "No comment."

"Your turn," he said. "Ask me something."

"What's your favorite food?"

"Why did you ask that?"

I shrugged.

"I don't like food," he said.

I rolled my eyes.

"Why did you roll your eyes?"

"Is that your next question?"

"Yes," he said.

"Because," I said. "You're fat."

"That might as well be the answer to everything," Paul said and he began to laugh. Only it wasn't a laugh, it was a wheeze. It was a snake hissing happily. He put up his hand and said, "I'm sorry. I'm sorry."

I stared at him, trying to hold a scowl, but the corners of my mouth twitched and soon I was laughing too. Two fat kids laughing together.

"Let's get real," I said.

He nodded, his chins quivering.

"What do you want to be when you grow up?"

"I'm already grown up. I can't grow anymore." He started laughing again.

"Seriously," I said.

"Serious," he said.

I wrote it down.

He asked me what I liked to do when I'm alone.

I told him I read fantasy and horror novels, but then I thought only the Geekiest or Nerdiest would say such a thing. "And I like video games," I added. "All day long."

Paul snorted. He said reading was like running away, and in his next question he asked what I was running away from.

"Nothing," I said. "I like to read."

"Sure you do," he said.

We finished the interview and Mr. B instructed us to report our findings. When it was our turn, Paul had slipped off to sleep. His head rested against the wall, his mouth slightly open.

Mr. B shook his head. "Paul," he said quietly.

Paul didn't wake.

"Paul," Mr. B said again. Mr. B always wore dress shirts that were a little too small, as if he wanted us to see all his working muscles.

Paul snored.

"Paul!" Mr. B's pecs bounced.

Paul startled awake.

Mr. B's shoulders were tight. He fisted the pen in his hand. He opened his mouth to say something and stopped. He opened it again, and this time everything gushed out. "Paul, you are going to die. Man, I hate to say it. But you are going to die because you're so fat. What are you going to do, Paul? What are you going to do with yourself? You fall asleep. You're always late. Pick yourself up, Paul. Pick yourself up, man. I don't want you to die. Do you want to die?"

Paul looked down at his meaty hands.

"Think hard, Paul. Think hard, man. I'm not kidding here."

I could tell Mr. B regretted what he said as soon as he said it. He wasn't a mean teacher. In fact, he was my favorite, the one who motivated me to write, the only teacher I kept in touch with after I graduated. He never criticized my fat. That day, however, his anger at Paul made him vulnerable. He looked at the chalkboard, digging his hands in his pockets, sighing deeply. Some snickered. A few laughed. Mr. B shot them a look and said shut up. He turned to me. "So," he said, "what did you learn about Paul?"

I looked over my list of questions and answers. I had the urge to come to Paul's rescue, to speak up against Mr. B and all who were laughing at Paul's expense. To tell them all to go fuck themselves. But I separated from him. I wasn't Paul Hutchkins fat. I wasn't Fattest, or Ugliest, or Weirdest.

Paul looked like he was about drift off again, his head wavering on his thick neck. Stay awake, Paul. Don't go. But it was too late, his eyelids fluttered and shut.

∽

A couple of days later, as Dan, Rob, and I walked home from school, we noticed a crowd near the football field. A crowd like that meant one thing: fight. We ran toward the crowd, pushing our way to the front.

Paul was trying to shake something off his ankles. He swung his backpack at his legs, trying to knock off this sliver of a kid attached by the teeth. Tommy W. Tommy had clamped his mouth around Paul's left ankle and wouldn't let go. Tommy was ninety pounds of evil, hair the color of a lit firecracker. When I was in elementary school, Tommy used to climb up to the top of my house and pee in the chimney, his penis waving in the air, his cackling laugh echoing down my block. Tommy held on to Paul's ankle. Paul made slow, muffled cries, then he toppled over. Fell on his front and rolled onto his back. When Paul fell, Tommy let go and launched himself in the air onto Paul's stomach. He did it again and again. Rob and Dan were friends with Tommy and said they wanted in. They were like kids at the playground waiting for their turn to go down the slide. When one went, the other waited. Paul had turned the color of a beet. I watched. I couldn't do anything else.

"This shit's a riot," Dan said.

"Come on, dude," Rob said to me. He threw himself on Paul and all I heard was Paul's expelled breath.

I shook my head. "Go ahead," I said. "This is funny."

Tommy turned to me. "Don't be a pussy," he said. "Or I'll fuckin' jump on your stomach." Tommy frightened me, even though I towered over him, even though I was sure I could hurl him like a javelin.

Paul's stomach rose and dropped. He lay still. I took two big steps and jumped, all my weight crashing down on him. He grunted when I landed. His mouth was wet with spit and sweat and maybe tears. His mouth was slightly open. He stared right at me through his slits. I backed away. Rob, Dan, and Tom took more turns. Paul stopped fighting, taking one launch after the other until a teacher came running out and chased everyone away. As I ran, I saw Paul's belly, a swell in the ground, a heaving, breathing piece of earth.

When Rob and Dan made it away from school, they started laughing. Rob and Dan said Paul's belly was like a sponge. No, jello. No, a tub of shit. I walked with my head down, trying to catch my breath. Heaviness settled in my chest. Tommy didn't say a word. His fingers were in his mouth. He kept picking stuff out of his teeth—threads of sock, pieces of skin.

&

The summer I turned twenty, I saw Paul Hutchkins again. I don't remember what happened to him after the fight with Tommy. Perhaps he dropped out. Perhaps he attended the other high school across town. Perhaps I had pushed him so far out of my mind, so the weight of my guilt didn't hang on me the remaining years of high school. Paul had disappeared, and with him, the images of that day.

Three years later, however, there he was, working the cash register at the mini-mart on 95th Street, not even a block away from the football field where he collapsed. He had gotten bigger. It was hard to believe that a boy who used to weigh over three hundred fifty pounds could become even larger, four fifty, maybe five hundred pounds. He didn't resemble a person anymore, but a wobbly blob. His flesh drooped and sagged, as if at any moment a part of him would drip off like wax and sizzle on the mini-mart floor. He was in a small booth, and his body filled the space. I wondered how he got in and out, wondered how he managed to breathe. A familiar feeling came over me, the same one that made me feel superior to Paul when he first arrived in OLCHS. I had been losing weight rapidly, sixty pounds in three months, but I was still fat, not the fattest, but fat enough.

Paul Hutchkins said very little as he rang out customers. He took their cash in chubby fingers and then dropped change into their palms. I wandered the candy aisles, taking peeks at him, his enormity. He sat on two stools, leaning against the display case of cigarettes behind him. A cartoon of Camel Joe stared at Paul behind darkened sunglasses. In that mini-mart, everything seemed in easy proximity to Paul, as if he was the star the worlds outside of him revolved around.

At the mini-mart, I got myself some gum and a Coke. I hoped Paul wouldn't recognize me. When I approached the checkout, Paul paused.

"I know you," he said. His voice was even deeper than I remembered it.

"Yeah," I said. "Hi, Paul. "We were in high school together."

"That's right." He began to chuckle and I looked behind him at the smokes.

"Can I have some Reds?" I said. "Hard pack."

"I have to see I.D.," he said. "It's the law."

We were the same age, but I didn't want to argue. I dug into my wallet, fetched out my driver's license and handed it to him.

He looked at it long and hard. "It doesn't look like you," he said.

"It is though," I said.

"I know," he said. "I'm just saying it doesn't look like you."

My eyes wandered around the mini-mart, my fingers tapping

on the counter. Paul was calm and cool.

"It's a bad picture," I said. "I was hung over."

"Says you're 180 pounds."

"So?"

"You're not one-eighty."

"It says what it says."

"I can read," he said. "I'm just saying you don't look one-eighty."

"Maybe I'm a little heavier."

"A little." He laughed.

"I'm in a hurry," I said. "I have to be somewhere."

He put his hand up, and it was as large as my face. "You're in a hurry? You have to go back to Carbondale?" He pointed to my license again. "It says you live in Carbondale. Where's that?"

"Six hours away. South."

"Why did you leave?"

"This place's a hole."

"Not really," said Paul. He waved his hand around the mini-mart like it was his kingdom, like there was no better place in the world than a store in Cook County.

Most of my friends believed so too. But to me, Cook County was a magnet that pulled you under. It wasn't just a pull. It was a pull and smother. It was a pull and suffocate. Rob was a mechanic at Jiffy Lube; Dan dished out popcorn at the movie theaters. They both drank too much and gambled their money away on long shots at the track. Whenever I returned home for break, I was initially glad to be back, but I also wanted to escape. The strange thing was I didn't know what I wanted or how I should go about getting it. I couldn't identify what the "it" was. I only knew that it was there and it sometimes put a lump in my throat, sometimes put me into such a quiet trance my friends would have to elbow me awake.

"What does Carbondale have?" Paul said.

"I go to school there."

He laughed like it was the funniest thing he'd ever heard. "What are you trying to be?"

"A writer."

"Have you published anything?"

"Yeah," I said.

"What magazine?"

"*Grassroots*."

"What roots?"

"Grass."

"I've never heard of it. What kind of magazine is that if I've never heard of it? I work here almost every day and read all the magazines I want. We got a lot. But I haven't heard of *Grassroots*. Can I get it at a bookstore or something?"

"Not really."

"Then where can I get one?"

"At the university."

"That's not a magazine," he said. "If it's a magazine, everyone can buy it."

"Whatever," I said.

Paul began to scan my things in, his eyes never leaving my face. He handed me the smokes and said, "These will kill you."

"So will anything else," I said.

"I'm just saying. I tried one and thought it tasted like tar. Not that I know what tar tastes like."

"How much for everything?"

"Easy there. Nothing's ever that urgent to get to." He looked at the register and told me it was two dollars and some change.

I dug into my wallet for a few pennies and dropped them into his waiting hand. He counted them. Counted them slowly. Then he pushed back one of the pennies. "We don't take crazy money," he said.

I blinked then looked down. I noticed the Queen of England on the penny instead of Abraham Lincoln.

"We only take American money."

I wanted to flee, to turn around and just leave Paul behind, leave all the memories of him in the mini-mart among the candy bars and cigarettes and windproof lighters. I fished in my pockets for more change and found a nickel. I gave it to him and told him to keep the change, ready to jet out, but he shook his head.

"I can't take gratuity. Against store policy."

"It's four pennies."

"Still," he said, smirking.

I reached out my hand and he put the four pennies in my palm. When his fingers grazed my skin, I flinched. He didn't move his fingers right away, but let them dangle over my hand for a moment longer.

"Thanks," I said. I started out the door.

"Hey," he said.

I stopped.

"Nice seeing you again."

I nodded and waved. He raised his arm and it was his smile I remember, wide and unnatural, like a carved pumpkin.

Later that day I met up with Rob and Dan at the bar. I told them I saw Paul. I told them he worked at the mini-mart on 95th. "What did he look like?" they asked. "Was he still a tub?" I smiled and said Paul looked like a million bucks, like the king of the world.

Secret

My father had a porno collection. Because I was alone most of the night—my parents worked the night shift—I was in the habit of snooping through their desks and drawers. At ten, I didn't know pornos existed. I don't even recall why I was searching through my parents' belongings, only that it felt good and wrong, and that combination, then and now, was overwhelmingly thrilling.

I found little in my mother's closet and drawers; I didn't expect to. She was too predictable, except for her anger, which could come at unexpected times.

My father, however—I marveled at my discoveries. He kept a manual of sexual positions under his side of the mattress—pencil drawn sketches of a man and woman engaged in a rambunctious game of Twister. In his desk was a nude deck of cards—vintage women—that I pocketed and hid in my comic book collection between *The Amazing Spider-man* and *Ghostrider*. In his sock drawers, condoms, which I thought were skin-colored balloons with an extra wide blowhole. In his briefcase of important documents, I discovered his porno.

I initially thought the VHS tapes were recordings of famous Thai funerals or weddings. My family loved to watch important Thai people, especially royalty. It made them feel like they were still home and not in a land of foreign faces and voices. There were five VHS tapes and nothing to indicate what they were. I took one and put it in the VCR.

The world suddenly opened up.

Once, sixteen years later, when I first got through a central New York winter, I waited to see if I could catch a tulip in blossom. I had been so desperate for color. Where I lived we could go for weeks without seeing the sun. My then-wife thought I was nuts, hovering over a tulip, wanting to see one actually open. For weeks, I watched. I imagined the stem rising from the ground, growing taller and taller. The tip would become bigger and bigger, like a tear ready to burst. And then, it would happen. It would open. I had fallen asleep on a folding chair, waiting, and when I woke up there it was, a tulip in full bloom. Despite my slumber, I felt as if I witnessed something extraordinary, something that stole my breath and quickened the heart.

That was how it felt that night, a blossoming of a different sort.

Tangled bodies. Sweat dripping onto bare backs. Thrust. Pause. Thrust. Moan. Pant. Moan. The mechanics of sex escaped me, but I couldn't deny that what I was witnessing was akin to dancing, one body responding to another, moving in synch or repelling violently off each other like opposite charged particles, which I had just learned about in science class.

There was a peculiarity, however. The women on my father's tapes were white—blonde, brunette, the occasional redhead. They were buxom in the ways the women at the Chicago Thai temple weren't. These were the women my mother told me to stay away from. The ones she spoke of in quiet whispered warnings. "Be careful, Tong. American woman too aggressive, want only one thing." It was exactly these warnings that made them much more appealing. Made me want that one thing, also.

It didn't surprise me that my father had videos like these. He was an admirer of the female form. At temple, he would tell stories to doctors's wives, charming them. They hung on his every word, smiling and touching his shoulder with vividly painted fingertips.

My father enjoyed their attention, craved it. He allowed his eyes to trail the movements of every beautiful woman. It was what got him into trouble a few years later, the unraveling of the family, a divorce that sent my mother into herself, and me with a ball of anger I couldn't reconcile. Still, I had assumed his gaze was reserved for Thai women. But here they were, white nakedness, as exotic to him, perhaps, as a rare tropical fish. Here they were, white women, fornicating on 120-minute VHS cassettes, hidden in a briefcase of important documents, which told me two things: he thought it was wrong, and it was a secret.

The Uncovering

Something is stuck, a disintegrating image of two boys on a tee-ter-totter—one up, one down—both of them looking at me—the viewer of this image—with disdain, as if I was responsible for the disruption of their fun, or worse yet, I am the bringer of all woe in the world that has yet to happen.

☙

It was 1982, and a lunar eclipse bloodied the moon and a musi-cian moonwalked across the stage with one glittering hand.

☙

This image in my head is of a photo that melted in my hands.

☙

Those boys, those looks—the creases and waves of consternation etched deep in the forehead, the narrowing of the mouth—those looks, frozen, ignite a strong sense of betrayal, which is like strip-ping the self of skin and making the rawness of the body visible.

☙

Jonathan Swift: "I never wonder to see men wicked, but I often wonder to see them not ashamed."

☙

Tip: Don't store photos in a basement.

☙

One of the boys is me.

☙

The other boy, whose name I have forgotten, was my best friend at the time, and my father would take me to my best friend's house and we'd do best friend things, like play cops and robbers, sing and dance to Thriller, read about planets and solar systems, ride a teeter-totter for hours.

ɛɔ

In a basement a photo can mold, can be nibbled by insects or rats, and if the photo is near a stack of wood or a rubber hose, both may contain traces of sulfur, which can trigger a slow deterioration—a fading, a yellowing.

ɛɔ

Two yellow boys on a teeter-totter—one going up, the other going down.

ɛɔ

In the photo, before it went way, was a yellow sky and yellowing grass and a yellow wooden fence behind us.

ɛɔ

Basements also flood.

ɛɔ

I am frozen at the highest point in my life.

ɛɔ

Our fathers sat in the kitchen, drinking beers—though I don't think my father drank because he was not a drinker and would turn the color of a sun-scorched beet when imbibing even a sip of alcohol—and comparing Buddha pendants most Thai men wore around their necks.

ɛɔ

My father wore three large Buddha pendants.

ɛɔ

The more Buddhas you wore the wealthier you seemed to be.

ɛɔ

We weren't rich, my father a textile factory worker, but he enjoyed the illusion of wealth.

છ

When my father walked he clinked.

છ

I had one Buddha and it was small because I was small and sometimes I imagined the Buddha around my neck pressing against my chest bone, trying to burrow into me or chase something out.

છ

My best friend did not have a Buddha, or I don't remember if he had one or not, because he being my best friend had nothing to do with Buddha.

છ

But his father had hundreds of Buddhas and he would line them up on a kitchen table and look at them through a loupe, which I found fascinating—how one eye squints to keep the loupe attached, how under the gaze of a loupe imperfections are made clear.

છ

I am imperfect.

છ

Polypropylene, a thermoplastic polymer, is the best way to protect photos from aging and is used in thermal underwear, packaging tape, and rope.

છ

My best friend—in photo, in memory—is perfect.

છ

Polypropylene cannot protect against a flooding basement.

છ

One day, after a quick summer storm, water poured into the basement through the circuit box, and underneath the box was an album of photos.

છ

What floated in the pond of the basement was one picture, a leaf in a current.

ဢ

If you've never seen a flood through a circuit box, imagine an amusement park ride where you plummet fifty feet into a pool of water and then someone throws in a plugged toaster.

ဢ

What is not in the photo: that moment a boy does a bad thing without thought and that bad thing still makes him shiver with guilt, a feeling he can't tolerate because it makes his inside shake, his fingers lose feeling, his head blur.

ဢ

What is not in the photo: when my best friend and I hid behind the bar in his basement, half empty bottles of liquor on shelves, the plush of the red carpet on our skins, and my best friend squeezed in my cheeks into a pucker and I did his, and we made each other sing "Billie Jean" or "Beat It" with our mouths in tiny little Os and how we laughed so hard his father screamed from the kitchen for us to shut up because we were disrupting the talk of Buddhas.

ဢ

I've seen those faces before, those grimaces.

ဢ

It lay wet between my fingers—that photo—and already the water was doing what water does to paper—distorting, destroying, disappearing.

ဢ

Also not in the picture: I pushed my best friend down the stairs.

ဢ

Edgar Allan Poe: "There was much of the beautiful, much of the wanton, much of the bizarre, something of the terrible, and not a little of that which might have excited disgust."

Oh Buddha, what had I done?

Sometimes when I look at the moon, I sense a change take hold of me, and it isn't anything like lycanthropy, but it is a taking, this feeling of being pulled or pushed.

~

Blame it on the moon, even though I don't remember whether the moon was out or whether it was night or day or what my best friend and I were doing before the push.

~

I'm not sure what came first, the stairs or the teeter-totter, but I stopped seeing my best friend not because I pushed him down the stairs, but because my best friend's father was an angry man.

~

Once, at temple, my best friend's father came roaring out of a small room, red-faced, Buddhas clinking and swaying on his chest, screaming at the women gathered in the hallway after afternoon prayers, saying they were inconsiderate rich bitches, yapping and yapping, while he was trying to pray in peace, and would they get the hell out of here so he could reconvene with Buddha.

~

I was scared of my best friend's father.

~

My best friend's father wore ten Buddhas around his neck.

~

He was a factory worker, too.

~

He had a twitch that reminded me of zombies.

~

He drank a lot of beer.

This is a not an excuse.

He let me sip his beer once.

None of those ten Buddhas stilled his hand when he punished my best friend.

What I remember: my best friend's face from the bottom of the stairs.

The flood took a lot, destroyed a lot, which I have since replaced or forgotten about.

I can't forget this.

Water is a type of cleansing.

When my father came to the stairs and saw my best friend at the bottom of it, he said, "What have you done?"

I don't remember what I said.

My best friend's father came with a loupe still in his eye.

He said my best friend must've tripped, and then returned to the kitchen table of a hundred Buddhas.

I don't remember much of my best friend now, why I even called him my best friend, except for that sin, except for a photo that used to exist, and the trick that photos can sometimes do of opening a door you have shut for a long time and keeping that door open—forever open—even when the photo became mush in my hands.

∽

I want to say I am not capable of pushing someone down the stairs.

∽

This would be a lie.

∽

We are all capable.

∽

Perhaps when my best friend looked up at me, he saw his father.

∽

Perhaps when I look back at me, I saw his father, too.

∽

Allison Croggon: "We are all mistaken sometimes; sometimes we do wrong things, things that have bad consequences. But it does not mean we are evil, or that we cannot be trusted ever afterward."

∽

But the self has a way of holding on, has a way of remembering, even thirty-four years later, of a sin caused by a boy with a small Buddha around his neck, and the quick, thoughtless push of a best friend down a flight of stairs.

∽

My best friend—unharmed—did not cry.

∽

I—harmed—cried/am crying/will continue to cry.

∽

In a couple of months, I will have a son named after the tree Buddha meditated under, and I worry about this world he will be born into.

I want to say to him, when he is ready: You can inflict hurt and will hurt in a way you will not expect, and then you will shoulder feelings of guilt and shame for the rest of your days, and there is nothing you can do but look at your hands and see their capabilities.

❧

Perhaps I won't mention any of this to him.

❧

Perhaps there is nothing I can say.

❧

I do not wear a Buddha around my neck anymore.

❧

I wet-vacuumed the concrete floors, cleared out everything that was destroyed, all those boxes of photos, all those boxes of things, and I wonder what other moments have I ridded myself of, what other guilts and joys and pains, and whether I am better without them or am somehow incomplete, undone, fractured.

Summer Days, 1983

I

He was Thai, not the strange and pale Catholic boys I palled with. My parents loved him because he was Thai, and I had no Thai friends. It did not matter that he was a high schooler who lacked high school friends. What mattered was how he took flight, bike like an appendage. How he and bike spun and twirled, how he and bike traversed the world on one wheel. How I was in awe, the on-looking second-grader, the boy watching his first Thai friend, Thai magician, Thai god.

II

This is what happened: lying in suburban grass, staring at the sky, the contrails of a plane landing at the airport a few miles away. He said, Easy life. He whistled. Easy everything. Words slipped out like water on rocks, vowels lingered longer from his lips. Easy, he said and bumped against my shoulder. Meanwhile, clouds took animal shapes, ants tickled the underside of my arm.

III

This is what happened: he stayed the night once, and we un-rolled the fold-out couch and lay underneath it past bedtime—he was Thai after all and Thais were allowed leniency. My parents succumbed to sleep hours earlier, the house dark except for Johnny Carson on TV, his white hair, his white suit, his white teeth, like a lighthouse.

IV

This is what happened: he pulled down his pants. Johnny Carson swung an imaginary golf club. Ed McMahon's guttural laugh.

V

This is what happened: he grabbed it tight in his hands and tapped my shoulder.

And this: he pointed at my pajama bottoms.

And this: Let me see yours.

And this: I slid my shorts down to my ankles.

And this: his hushed laughter, *laik*, small in Thai.

VI

Years later, when I was in high school, I would see him at a Chicago party, beer in hand, beautiful white girl on his arm. How I envied him again, envied the ease of which he stood and talked to everyone at the party. How he seemed a sun that planets revolved around. How this woman, lips like peppers, touched and traced his cheeks with a red fingernail.

When he saw me, his eyes widened, his smile widened, his sinewy arms widened to embrace me. He said I had grown. *Yai*, big. Asked if I remembered that summer, those days of bike and sky. You look good, he said. A man.

VII

I tell a lover the story. We are in bed, the southern Illinois sun filtering through the laced curtains, her dogs lying in patches of light. She tells me it's not normal, but it didn't feel wrong then nor does it now, only a memory without anchor. She says I have stored this memory in a dusty corner of my brain.

Perhaps.

Perhaps this is what we do, sometimes, to endure. Perhaps we wish these moments away like an eyelash, like dandelion fuzz.

When he comes back, it is without sentiment, a dropped rock in water, ripples and ripples, spreading and spreading. What remains is a drawing left too long in the rain, the faint lines of chalk, a world empty of grace and color.

Twitch, Blink, Shiver

The outside world frightened my mother. So much so she rarely ventured outside the house, finding herself sitting in front of the bay windows of her Chicago home day after day and sewing Thai dresses she would seldom wear. She watched the daily comings and goings of the neighborhood—the little girl who did endless tricycle loops in our driveway, the black mutt that barked at any passerby from the front yard, and our neighbor Jack always riding on his lawn mower. This was a foreign landscape. Everything about America scared her—the language, the food, the weather.

But not horror movies.

Horror movies delighted her the way a baby is delighted by rattle-y things.

Some time in the nineties, my mother rented *Child's Play* and hadn't laughed as loud at a movie since. *Child's Play* was about a single mother who buys her son a demonic doll, Chucky. Chaos ensues. I was maybe a sophomore in high school and pretended not to be scared at my mother's movies anymore. I was her lone movie watching companion because my father couldn't stomach horror movies, and when he left after the divorce, my mother's fear of America grew exponentially. The more she feared, the more she watched horror movies. When I was six or seven, I hid under blankets when we watched *The Shining* or *Halloween*. The older I got, I found ways to calm my fears. I laughed along with her, talked through the scariest parts to distract myself. Sometimes, I would get up to go to the bathroom when I knew a slaying would happen.

The truth: I was a scaredy-cat.

When alone, every sound had a source, and every source was something out to kill me. I slept with the lights on and made sure all closets and doors were closed. I inherited my mother's fear, her sense of displacement.

I was not afraid of Chucky, though. Chucky was an ugly doll in overalls and red hair, freckles dotting the top of his cheeks. Chucky was nowhere near as frightening as the doll in *Poltergeist*. That doll dwells in my nightmares. Chucky was not even as scary as the doll in the window of the Doll House on Meade Avenue. Often, at night, my best friend Mike and I walked around the neighborhood, talking about our crushes, about our futures. Meade had no lights, just a long dark block. Tree branches looked like fingers dangling over us. On full moon ventures, our shadows elongated across the blacktop.

The Doll House.

There wasn't anything unusually scary about the house itself. It was a regular brown-bricked suburban bi-level, similar to my house. Except for the doll in the front window. Each day the doll had a new outfit, sometimes a new hairstyle. It was a shiny-faced porcelain doll, one of those old fashioned ones that always gave me the creeps.

Mike and I always stopped in front of the Doll House. We stared at it. We freaked ourselves out.

"It moved," I whispered. "Did you see it move?"

"Holy fuckin' shit," said Mike.

The longer we stared, the doll did more things. Twitched. Blinked. Shivered.

"Kiss it," Mike said one night. "I dare you."

"Whatever," I said.

"You scared?"

"No."

"Scared little Thai boy." He laughed, but I could tell he was scared too. The night seemed darker that day, seemed to envelope us in a humid blanket.

"I'm not," I said. "I'll prove it."

I walked up the driveway, turning to look at Mike one last time, hoping he'd let me off. He shooed me with the back of his hand.

Each step felt heavy, like the one time I trampled through my mother's just watered garden, trampling her tomatoes and bitter melons.

I was at the window.

The doll's eyes followed my movements.

I jumped back.

"Kiss it," said Mike.

I gathered up my courage, knelt down, my hands on the base of the front window. I imagined the doll's lips puckering up. I closed my eyes.

Then the kiss.

Quick.

Cold.

Like any first kiss.

When I opened my eyes I was already running toward Mike who was bent over laughing, saying, "That was fuckin' great."

I laughed too, loud, just to hear something disturb the night's quiet.

For the rest of the year, kissing the doll became a ritual. We each took turns. We dared each other to do more adventurous things. Stare at it for a minute. French kiss the doll. Kiss it with our asses. We were fifteen and overcoming our fears of the night, of monsters, of ghosts; we were fifteen and both of us still slept with stuffed animals and both of us were smoking a pack of Reds a day;

we were fifteen, at the cusp of entering a different world. We tested our fear; we tested our sense of adolescent freedom.

༄

When my mother packed to move back to Thailand in 2004, retiring after over thirty years as a nurse, I retraced the route Mike and I took when we were fifteen. It was daylight. The avenue was different in the sun, plain and simple as any suburban neighborhood. At the Doll House a woman watered pansies in the front yard. The doll stood in the window, as I remembered it. I approached the woman and introduced myself. I told her a friend and I used to dare each other to kiss the doll. We did this for a year. We made up corny stories, but we never knew the truth.

She smiled. "I used to clean mysterious smudges off the window each morning. That was you?"

I nodded. Smiled.

Then she sighed and told me about her daughter, who loved that doll, her special doll, the one she bought for her. During the summer her daughter drowned at a swimming lesson at the high school. It was a memorial to her, something she couldn't let go, something she needed to preserve.

I thanked her for her time, but I wanted to say more. I wanted to tell her how in daylight the doll was gorgeous—the shine of her skin, the perfect curls. I admired and understood the care and the time she took to preserve a memory. A memory that I now shared. A memory I have reshaped. In one window was this doll, in another was my mother. Both looking out. Both waiting for something to happen.

The doll had ingrained itself into my past. It carried with it a strange nostalgic quality, like my mother's horror movies and all horror movie monsters of my past, like Freddy Krueger and his razor glove, like Mike Myers and his featureless mask, like Chucky and his iconic overalls. These things took on new meanings beyond fear. They were part of a larger web, which included this doll in the window on Meade Avenue. In the years to come, in the light of remembrance, that doll will forever twitch, blink, and shiver.

IV.

A Sequence of Thoughts
Without Any Kind of Order

Seven

Lately, time seems to be all I think about on a personal and philosophical level. Perhaps it's because I notice age slowing down the ones I love. Perhaps I discovered more gray nose hairs in my right nostril and that freaked me the hell out. Or perhaps this awareness of time comes when our sense of self gets challenged, like mine has in the last few months.

When you think about time, you are really thinking about death.

Ninety-one

This should not be a surprise to you: Time rules us. We do not and cannot control it. As much as I wanted to possess superhuman powers when I was a teenager—like slowing time with a snap of my fingers when my eighth grade crush Brenna Murphy—having undergone wonderful changes of the body—ran towards me, I could not. I lived by the laws of time, subjected to a two-month relationship with Brenna that involved hand holding, park kisses, and her chasing me with a butcher's knife.

Time is an unavoidable fixture in our existence. We live by it. We sleep according to time. We arrange meetings, lectures, and classes by time. We watch our favorite shows and take our medication at certain times. How often do we check the time of the day? How often do we ask, "What time is it?" How many times do we wish for more time to write a meditation on time, a memoir about a certain time of life, or a letter to an ex-wife or a dying parent? How many times have we wished for more time to do all the things we want to do?

It is not surprising then that the English lexicon is infested with clichés of time. All in due time. There's no time like the present. Time after time. Time and again. Time flies.

Nor is it surprising that writers and philosophers have been contemplating time since the dawn of time.

From Plato: "And so people are all but ignorant of the fact that time is really the wanderings of the sun and the planets."

Sophocles: "Hide nothing, for time, which sees all and hears all, exposes all."

St. Augustine in his *Confessions*: "What then is time? If no one asks me, I know: if I wish to explain it to one that asketh, I know not."

Twenty-five

The holiday season approaches. The landscape of America changes. The department stores glitter in silver and gold garland. Santa is everywhere with his jolly cheeks and cotton-tipped hat. Bing Crosby croons holiday songs in the grocery stores, and bells beg for donations in a red pail.

Holidays are ripe for nostalgia. They are moments to assess our lives. We move forward. We move backwards. We think whether this holiday will be better than the last. We begin, as most children do, to dream of new toys Santa will sneak under the Christmas tree.

Even as a Buddhist, I'm inundated with holiday moments, memories from years past. A mental rolodex of Christmases and New Years. My father and his new Polaroid. The shutter and flash. The seconds it took for the picture to materialize. Aunty Sue carving the Chinatown duck, her hands and knife thick with yummy grease. My mother's soft snores on Christmas Eve after working a double shift at the hospital.

Eight

Before my mother moved back to Thailand, she gave me two large boxes of photo albums. I went through each of them, trying to remember our former lives, stilled in photographs. What struck me most were not only the photos of our holidays, but my mother's perfect print next to the yellowing photos. The date. The time. The place.

I've seen this impulse to record in other photo albums. What is this need we possess not only to capture the photo, but to log it in with numbers? Do the numbers mean anything?

I am standing in bright neon pants that flare at the bottom. A blue octopus is on my head. Behind me is the Christmas tree, delicate ornaments glinting from the camera's flash. I'm smiling. Two of my front teeth are missing.

Beside the photo, my mother's writing: Ira, age three, living room, Oak Lawn, Illinois, 12/25/79. He is happy.

Two Thousand

Every time I see numbers in an essay, I hear Dick Clark's voice counting down to the new year. I also think of the apocalypse. I know these two things don't go together.

Thirty-seven

I've been through thirty-seven Christmases and thirty-seven New Years. After a while, it's one big mess. A fun, festive mess, like discarded and torn wrapping paper, like bows and ribbons on your pets.

One Point Eight

Every year I go to Thailand to visit my mother and Aunty Sue. They are eighty, and now time has slowed their walks, hunched their backs, clogged their ears, much to my impatient dismay. Now, I help them in and out of cars. I hold them as they walk up and down stairs.

At the Chiang Mai Airport, they play with an eight-month-old baby, who smiles and gurgles and drools happiness. They make faces at him and coo. They caress the smoothness of his skin.

I watch them and think, this baby is me. Both my mother and aunt are really cooing at me, or a version of me that no longer exists, but one cataloged in their memory, a moment they have stilled to relive, a joy that can never return.

But it has.

Everything they do, everything they eat, is in relationship with the past. It's in the manner of their speech. In the moments when they begin, "Back then...." It's even in how they hold me—longer, stronger, never wanting to let go.

A Gazillion

The memoirist, like my aging parents, does not want to let go either. It's as if he is in a sci-fi movie, where his memories are displayed in front of him. And he uses his hand to arrange them, moves them around, throws some out. He rewinds. Fast forwards. He does this so that he can create a narrative timeline. The first steps of telling a story. The first steps of understanding.

Forty-one

I've become a reluctant fan of the writer David Shields, author of the controversial book, *Reality Hunger: A Manifesto*. If one were to flip through *Reality Hunger*, one would find an array of criticism against chronology. One would find Shields's championing of fragmentation and mosaic movements. One would find lines like this: "Anything processed by memory is fiction." Or, "Everyone who writes about himself is a liar."

Reality Hunger is Shields's own manifesto, his way of understanding the world—he has said as much in interviews—but part of me turned into that gruff Chicago boy from ages ago, that Chicago boy defending his turf, his little tiny patch of city green because I had just published a memoir about being raised Thai in America and it was chronological and for the past ten years I have devoted myself to this genre. I was like, what the hell, dude? You best step off.

But what also lingered underneath this sentiment was a voice that said, "David's right, you know." He is. To a point.

After reading his manifesto, I wanted to see how his manifesto translated into his own work, so I picked up *The Thing About Life Is That One Day You'll Be Dead*.

Shields uses two threads to tell his story—one orders the memories he has of his father, never chronological, but fragmented and scattered in no specific pattern, and one discusses how the body ages and begins to deteriorate over time. Let me warn you: If you are a hypochondriac and do not want to be aware what happens at what age, avoid this book. I found myself counting the amount of hair I was losing and gauging my libido on a daily basis.

Despite Shields's diatribe against chronology in *Reality Hunger*, *The Thing About Life Is That One Day You'll Be Dead* is both chronological and a memoir. (David Shields's nose is probably itchy right now.) It is not chronological in the traditional sense, nor is it a memoir in the traditional sense. In his book, Shields's father escapes the linear because there is nothing linear about him. He is an enigma, a delicately curved question mark. Shields can't reconcile what he feels for his father, whether it is hate or deep affection. His memories of his past jump back and forth through time, in no logical sense. But we are never lost in the book because Shields has given us chronology, has imposed order, by telling us about time in the biological sense. Our bodies—our physical presences—are about time. It is the one constant thing that makes us human.

Twenty-three

David McGlynn, "Traumatized Time": "One of the magical qualities of creative nonfiction...is its ability to travel through time, to leap without preamble or warning from the narration of particular past events to the immediate and universal present."

One Billion Eight Hundred Thirty-three Million Five

Maybe the countdown to a new year and the countdown to the apocalypse aren't so different. If there is a beginning then there is an end.

One

I have to tell you this story. And it has to be chronological.

There was once a boy so insecure with his life, he took diet pills, believing that they would magically make him better. But he did not know what better meant. Skinnier? Happier? Normal-er? He didn't have the sense, this boy, to ask the questions necessary in understanding the self. He didn't want to understand the self. He didn't want to be anywhere in his head, where thoughts whirled and stabbed, where shadows sought to suffocate. He wanted a quick fix, a present-moment action. What's easier than popping pills? What's easier than taking a handful of them and washing it down with a swig of beer?

Oh, that boy, oh how he smiled and laughed, oh how he was proud that his appetite had shrunk to nothing. It was as if a stone wall had risen up in his digestive system and turned away all thoughts of food. He snacked on one potato chip a day. He drank one bottle of water. And at night, if he was good, he allowed himself a piece of candy, which he immediately hated himself for.

It did not matter that his friends began worrying about him, how shallow his cheeks became, how his moods were erratic, how he wasn't losing weight but starving weight off of him.

But look at him. He was beautiful—wasn't he? People loved the new him—didn't they? Look at him. He had lost fifty pounds in two months. Look at the ladder rungs of his rib cage. Look at the veins that worm through his hands. Look at his face that has become skeletal.

Look. Look. Look.

The story of this boy is chronological because it is a story of his body. It is a story about the changes of his body—inside and outside. Because his body was once fat, and day by day, his body expelled that fat. Time did that. His body recorded time. His body felt it.

But chronology is also important because there comes a moment when the boy finally registers fault. We need that moment of redemption, of change, because when the boy decides what he is doing is detrimental, it is a marker of change in his life. And then begins the process of healing, and the process of healing takes time.

Two

Cormac McCarthy, *All the Pretty Horses*: "Scars have the strange power to remind us that our past is real."

Seventy-seven

In Bernard Cooper's essay, "Marketing Memory," he states that if you want to preserve memory in its purest state, do not write a memoir. Suddenly, your past becomes a book—shaped, contained, revised and revisited language.

Imagine memory as a big messy glob of clay. A writer then begins to work at it. Press and fold. Cut the excess. Give detail to where there was once nothing. We do this for hours, days, years. We live in our heads. And finally, by the end of it all, our messy memory is not a blob of clay. Finally we have something presentable, readable, compressed, conflated.

The detritus of our clay?

We throw it in the trash. We discard it because now there is no use in keeping something that doesn't serve our narrative.

One Thousand Ten

The ball dropping. The bomb dropping.
I'm sorry I keep coming back to this.
Happy holidays.

Thirteen Point Thirteen

Let's get right to it. Writing a memoir, writing chronologically, is an unnatural act. (David, I agree with you.) But the artist makes the unnatural seem natural. The artist, the good artist, creates her art in such a way we do not question veracity. We just live it. We just follow. We say, Take us wherever you please.

Sixty-five

Lidia Yuknavitch, *The Chronology of Water*: "Events don't have cause and effect relationships the way you wish they did. It's all a series of fragments and repetitions and pattern formations. Language and water have this in common . . . All the events of my life swim in and out between each other. Without chronology. Like in dreams. So if I am thinking of a memory of a relationship, or one about riding a bike, or about my love for literature and art, or when I first touched lips to alcohol, or how much I adored my sister, or the day my father first touched me—there is no linear sense. Language is a metaphor for experience. It's as arbitrary as the mass of chaotic images we call memory . . ."

Ten

How does one talk about time when time loses meaning? As a person who has gone through depression, I begin to notice, retrospectively, that time has no significance. You are late. You miss meetings. You don't take the medications you should to get better. You sit in stasis, frozen, a body without a mind, a body without control. You no longer sleep. You no longer eat. Your mind—forever timeless—consumes you, but you spend every moment in this whirlwind of non-linear thoughts.

This is not reserved for the depressed. How about memoirs about abuse, addiction, illness, life-altering accidents, death? How does time affect the narrator? How does time affect the structure of a book? As writers, how can we remain faithful to chronology when our internal chronology is in so much flux?

The answer: we can't.

I'm not kidding.

As a writer, you are battling two things that prevent this: 1) memory and all its flaws 2) capturing a time in life where time no longer exists.

Einstein said the distinction between the past, present, and future is only a stubbornly persistent illusion. A memoirist is creating an illusion. This is as post-modern as it gets. The writer of memoir is creating a simulacrum, like reenactments of crimes on Court TV. As Buddha said, "Do not dwell in the past, do not dream of the future, concentrate the mind on the present." And it occurs to me that all memoirs are seen through this lens. Our pasts are filtered through the gaze of the present, and it is this present that begins to sift, sort and build that narrative.

Eighteen

When I was four, I peed on Santa's lap at Ford City Mall in Chicago. Or was I five? Or three?

I'm forgetting.

But this is not forgotten. I peed on his lap. And he was pissed.

Ten Thousand Eight Hundred Fifty-nine

The writing of a memoir is about not letting go. It is not the western psychological therapy of writing it down to expel thoughts and emotions. It's just the opposite. It's about writing it down to understand and live and relive and learn. The writing of a memoir is what Lauren Slater wrote once in an interview: "I, for one, expect my readers to be troubled; I envision my readers as depressed, guilty, or maybe mourning a medication that failed them. I write to say, 'You are not the only one.'"

One-Half

I just asked my mother to end this for me. She asked me what the topic is. I told her time and Christmas and writing.

"Tell them," she said, "that everyone dies." Then because she is Buddhist and believes in reincarnation, she added, "But you get to be in line again to do it all over."

The memoir writer is in line again and again. The memoir writer defies time. He goes back, goes forward, stays still. He relives, recreates, reimagines. It's a ride, you see, and a memoir writer can't get sick on it. He has to get in line again and again, before what? Time runs out? Time stops. Time stands still?

Impossible.

Maybe we are all waiting for something to drop.

A Meditation on Pain

"And once it comes, now that I am wise in its ways, I no longer fight it. I lie down and let it happen. At first every small apprehension is magnified, every anxiety a pounding terror. Then the pain comes, and I concentrate only on that."

—Joan Didion, "In Bed"

It's happening, says the woman I love to someone in the other room. The someone is most likely her sister, and I hear the shuffle of clogs on the ruined carpet, the swish and swirl of her turquoise dress. I feel the shadow of her body in the doorway. I hear her breathing, tiny bursts of air through the nose and mouth. I feel and hear everything, but I am not a body. And because I am no longer a body, I do not register sound or voice. I do not register anything. Even my presence on the scratchy carpet. I do not know that I have been lying in the lap of the woman I love as she soothes my sweat-drenched hair, as she whispers that this will pass. I do not hear her because I do not have ears. I do not have eyes. I do not see the hazy outline of her humid-frizzed hair or the worry etched in her face or how she looks down at me and then out the window, out past the dilapidated houses of this rundown block in Lafayette, Colorado, past the Rockies rising in jagged edges to snowy peaks, past logical explanation. Because right now, I do not register logic. Because this pain is not logical. This pain makes me whimper, makes me produce a noise that is octaves higher and sharper than

I can otherwise make. I become a supplicant to its needs. I have a mouth. Of this I am sure. I have a mouth but it acts without my guidance. Saliva seeps from corners. Lips chapped as cracked earth. The woman I love feeds me water. I sip from a straw, but all of it dribbles out from the corners of my mouth. All of it wetting my cheeks and chin, like a child sloppy with food. I am a child. I am helpless. I am without strength. I am without will. I believe I might die. That this might be the end of me, this moment. I believe that death would be a relief from it all.

Hang on, she says. It's almost over, she says. The end is in sight, she says.

☙

I want to tell you about a headache. I want to tell you when someone says they are having a headache we never take it seriously. We say go get some sleep. We say relax. We say it's only a headache. I want to say there are seven different types of pain medication in my medicine cabinet right now, and I've used all of them. Two of them are prescribed. One can knock me out for twenty-four hours and leave my mouth sandpaper dry. I want to tell you that a headache made me overdose on pain medication once, and all I remember was lurching up my lunch at the student health clinic in Carbondale, Illinois, and a beautiful nurse patting my back because I was crying at the same time, crying and lurching, crying and lurching, because the pain didn't go away, the one in my head, the one pulsating like a heart about to explode. I want to tell you that I know someone who had a headache and the only way he got rid of it was he shot himself. I want to tell you that I've thought about shooting myself.

☙

Testimonial from clusterheadaches.com:
  "I keep telling myself that I am strong enough to deal with it.

I've been doing it for a long time now. But then the next one hits, and I become a w[h]impering little baby with no strength what-so-ever."—Marcus

</p>

Q: How did it start?

A: It started like fairy tales do: once there was a peaceful land, and then black clouds gathered and lightning lit forests on fire and the talking animals scurried away; their cries for help were drowned by the rain that pelted the land in savage punches. And suddenly, there was no sound, the world on mute, and a blanket covered the sky, thick and suffocating. This was the apocalypse. This was the world's end. This was the kiss-your-ass-good bye moment. A baby hedgehog shivered in the corner of a hollowed out tree stump. A prince fell off his steed. A princess screamed until she was hoarse.

Am I being dramatic?

Yes.

No.

Absolutely not.

</p>

Cluster headaches. Suicide headaches.

A female sufferer likened the pain to giving birth to a hundred babies at once without epidural. Some sufferers have banged their heads repeatedly against brick walls, turning their foreheads to mangled meat. Some have attempted to take power tools, drills in particular, to the source of the pain. Some have begged friends and family members to end their misery.

Once, when the pain came, I grabbed for a knife, my fist tight around it, contemplating digging out my right eye. I was twenty-one. When the pain passed, I realized I grabbed the blade instead of the handle.

A four-inch cut almost to the bone.

A pool of blood on the flower-patterned couch, like the stain from a murder.

❧

"It's somewhere between 11:00 p.m. and 3:00 a.m., and I wake terrified, hopeful that I'm dreaming, and knowing that I'm not . . . I am careful not to wake the children as I make my way down the stairs. If they were to witness my nightly cluster ritual, they would never see me the same way again. Their father, fearless protector, diligent provider, crawling about in tears, beating his head on the hard wood floor." —Anonymous

❧

By nature, the cluster headache is consistent. For me it came every other year since I was fifteen. It came at roughly the same time each day—about two p.m. and lasted for two hours. It came and settled in my life for a period of six weeks, and afterwards it would leave, disappear, become a trembling memory.

The headache was an unwanted guest. And my unwanted guest was a serial killer with an ice pick. When the right side of my face started to tingle, I would announce, "He's coming." This headache became personified. This pain took a pronoun. I planned my days around him, like how I planned my travels around snow when I lived in upstate New York. In my daily planner, I blocked out the hours between one and six. I would be occupied during those times, writing in my planner: "Down time."

❧

The woman I love and I often joke that when a headache happens there is one sure way of getting rid of it: decapitation.

❧

Q: When did it start?
A: It started one day.

One day.

One day.

And I remember it.

I remember it.

Remember it.

And I repeated myself in threes, my brain as flighty as a jun-co, my concentration leaping in a million avenues in milliseconds. The sun filtered through the high school window, and I thought it was too bright, and I thought someone should dial down the light, and I said in my Southside Chicago voice, "Dial down that fuckin' light." The sprinklers chattered on the football field, and I could hear it two floors up, and it sounded like someone stuttering the word cheetah, and I said, "That shit's too loud. Too loud. Too fuckin' loud." And the bell rang and I sat in Mrs. B's American lit-erature class, my sophomore year, and we were going over *A Wrin-kle in Time*, a book I had read years before. And then my right eye blurred. And then Mrs. B's voice became muffled, as if she spoke through cotton. And then pain, a music of pain, sharp thumping, a heartbeat in the temples. Drumming, thrumming, strumming. And then I closed my eyes and I pulled at my hair. I could hear my roots creak. Pain.

Someone was stabbing me,

> stabbing me,
>
> stabbing me.

In the right eye,

> right eye,
>
> eye.

I had stepped through L'Engle's tesseract, her fictional inter-di-mensional portal that carried Meg, Charles and Calvin away from the world. But I wasn't among centaurs or the Black Thing. I was on a planet of red. Hazy red. Pulsing red. Pumping blood. A bleeding rose. Dripdripdrip, and thorns were piercing the inner cavities of my brain, blood blossoming, dripdripdrip, and the pain was delicious because I was crying. I was silently crying. And someone far off said, "Mrs. B, Ira's crying." And I could hear people turning to stare,

stare,

stare,

shifting in their chairs, and someone said, "He's probably crying because of Jean Lind," but I wasn't because Jean Lind—though she broke my heart—was not stabbing,

stabbing,

stabbing me

in the eye. Jean Lind was a pain of a different sort, and right then, she didn't matter because the world was about pain—the physical kind—the kind that erases all your woes, a pain so intense it steals your ability to speak, because when Mrs. B asks you if you are OK, you can't say anything. You manage to shake your head, and someone says, "His right eye is closed," and it was because pain had stolen my eye, had plucked,

plucked,

plucked it out of the socket. And

my boys, my Chicago boys, were like, "Dude, what's up?" And Mrs. B says, "Take him to the nurse," but I couldn't move,

move,

move,

until fingers laced under my arms and lifted me out of my seat, and I don't remember anything after that. Only that I woke in a cot. Only that my tears had stained the pillowcase, and the only pain left was a slight throb, a slight pulse in my temples, the fading remains of a sidewalk chalk drawing.

‹›

I do not consider myself a weak person. I am over six feet tall, over three hundred pounds. I have the build of a professional football linebacker—more fat than muscle—and I have a high tolerance for pain, loving long hours under a tattooist's needle, loving my strange little quirks like pressing bruises and scorching my body in a hot shower or playing with the fire of a candle. Once, I stabbed my hand with a pencil because of a stupid adolescent dare and it stuck.

I don't say these things to brag. I say these things to try to explain pain. The pain I felt when experiencing a cluster headache is intolerable. I would crumble under it. I would do almost anything to get rid of it. I understand why some soldiers collapse under torture, understand weakness, understand helplessness.

This is not about headaches. This is about tolerance. This is about pain and how it has the ability to crumple us.

໑

My family is plagued with migraines. My mother doesn't have them—she's thankful—but her four other sisters are cursed, especially the twins. This is what they call headaches, a curse carried over from another life. My aunts tell me I must've suffered a terrible death in my past life. An elephant crushing my skull, perhaps. Or a spear through the eye. Their mother had cluster headaches, my grandmother, a woman who died before I was born. On days when pain settled between her temples, she moved like a ghost, her hands over her eyes to block the harsh Thai light, her feet shuffling on teak floors. She would respond in nods and grunts, but she still managed to take care of all nine kids while Grandfather worked at the government office in town. My mother said she was a strong woman, but strong is an understatement. Strong doesn't fully capture what it is like to endure pain and still be productive, to still exist in the world of the living. Because headaches, bad headaches, terrifying headaches, horrifying headaches, propel us out of ourselves and we dwell somewhere no living being can reach.

The twins have them once a week, and on those days, their doors are closed to the world. And on those days we walk silently, speak in whispers.

☙

I've tried pure oxygen bars and deep meditation. I've tried weekly massages and chiropractic adjustments. I've tried fancy pillows and even fancier beds. I've tried acupuncture and eastern medicine. Nothing worked. But if you offered me a list of other things to try, I would. I would have climbed Everest, if I believed it would take the pain away. I would offer to be locked in a tiny room of spiders, one of my great fears, if I thought it would help.

☙

Q: Why did it start?

A: Who the fuck knows?

Ten doctors, seven specialists, five MRIs, twenty-five x-rays of the spine, uncountable blood tests. No one could determine what was wrong.

"Are you sure you're not exaggerating about this pain?" one doctor said. Earlier in the year, when I broke my ankle, he said I had ogre feet.

I nodded. "I'm not exaggerating."

"Are you sure it's not psychological then?"

"I'm fifteen," I said. "Everything's psychological."

Two years later: "You're normal," another doctor said.

"This is anything but normal."

"Your tests," he said, "All normal."

"If you knew how I felt, normal would not be a word you'd use."

I didn't blame the doctors. Though at the time, I wanted to bludgeon each one of them. I wanted to take a scalpel to the right side of their faces. "You see," I wanted to say. "This is what I feel. But worse. Much, much worse." I cried most days. I cried just thinking about the pain. I cried when the pain arrived. I cried when the pain left. I cried the whole day, and I was not a crier—in fact, I was and am adamantly against crying. But crying was all I could do. This pain reduced me into a shell of a person—no—I wasn't a person. I was a gelatinous mass of pain.

ev

I was a rarity. I suffered from something only a sliver of the human population had. When doctors said this, it was as if I had won a prize, something I should be proud of.

My winnings? Pills.

I had a collection of them, different sizes and colors. I took them like M&Ms.

Once, in the midst of pain, I chewed one and it tasted like a cloud of chemicals, acrid and chalky. Sometimes I passed out and did not remember where I was. Sometimes, most of the time, the pills failed to work and the pain persisted, like a megaphone in the ear, like an artist chipping on the inside of my eyelids, like a truck rolling over my head, and for the rest of the day I was a zombie— body without mind, movement through murky water.

ev

The Colorado Shakespeare Festival is going on in Boulder, and my favorite play "A Midsummer's Night Dream" starts at seven. My headache comes late today, after five. If we wait it out, we'll miss the play. I don't want to miss the play, don't want to miss one of my favorite literary characters, Puck, cause mischief in the world.

I organize a plan a couple hours before the headache arrives. I've packed a cooler with cold compresses and bottles of water. I've cleaned out the back of the Nissan station wagon, filled the back seat with pillows and an oversized stuffed animal of a white tiger, which I've named Cheyenne. For reasons unclear to me, I love to burrow my head into the scruff of his mane when the headache hits. I moan into his plushness, weep into his synthetic fur, beat my fists into his cottony cush.

"I'm not missing this fuckin' play," I say. "Fuck the headache."

The woman I love says, "Are you sure?" She sighs.

I know my headaches are hard to witness. But day after day, she stays with me, whispers to me, lets me hold her hand a little too tightly. I love this woman for sticking through my bouts of pain, but I know my headaches have taken a toll on her too. How tired she looks. How she has very little appetite for anything other than chocolate. How she stays up after I have passed out, because her adrenaline leaves her anxious and worried.

For this reason alone we are not missing "A Midsummer's Night Dream" because of this fuckin' headache, like we've missed planned hikes in the Rockies, like we've missed dinners with friends, like we've missed picnics in wildflower meadows.

"Everything is in place," I say. "This is the perfect plan."

And then he comes. There is a moment of lucidity, a moment where my muscles relax. It's like the green-time before a tornado, when the earth stills before havoc ensues. "He's coming," I say. This is the last lucid sentence I utter for the next two hours.

The woman I love nods.

We put our plan into motion. I get into the back of the car and lie down, dark sunglasses on. Already the light is too bright, and the first stab happens in the cortex of my right eye. I suck in a slurpy breath.

It's happening.

The woman I love says, "It's OK." She turns on the a/c full blast, but I don't feel it. I am gone. The rest of the car ride is a radiant blur. I'm told I cursed a lot, alternating between fuckshit-fuckshitfuckshit and other nonsensical words and sounds. I'm told that I bit into Cheyenne's ear and screamed. I don't remember how I got into the seat of the outdoor theater. I imagine the woman I love carrying me like an elderly hospital patient. I don't remember much, except when the curtains parted, my headache left me, and I grabbed for the woman I love's hand and squeezed, lightly, a pulse, to tell her I am back, to tell her I'm OK, to tell her thank you.

જ

"...I feel so helpless when it comes to comforting him. After a while it starts taking its toll on me and our children. I dre[a]d for the night to come..." —Loretta

જ

Q: When did it end?

A: Has it?

I don't know. I look around corners, waiting for him to return. I wish to be rid of him forever, but I understand what I wish for is unrealistic. The cluster headache, you see, always comes back.

It's been fourteen years since my last cluster headache. I remember that last pain. Remember the magnitude of that pain. In Stephen Kuusisto's essay, "Flawless Memory," he writes that memory theorists say that humans misremember experience and that our misapprehension becomes our experience. But like Kuusisto, when faced with such extreme pain—witnessing his mother in a malfunctioning hospital bed with an open chest cavity—theory goes out the window, and our memory of that moment shapes us, haunts us.

This pain haunts me. This headache.

That last pain—how it shook me, how it was so intense I found myself on my knees in front of the toilet in Gunnison, Colorado, a rented cabin, losing my dinner, the one I love watching from the bed, helpless. The next day, we rode a ski lift up Mt. Crested Butte, the wildflowers blooming on slopes of green, and I asked her to marry me.

It seems too perfect—doesn't it?—that this pain should leave me then, that it hasn't come back, that it remains in remission. It seems like a horrible, unrealistic short story, one where I would tell my student that the world doesn't work like this. I would tell him to go back and make me believe this moment. But the truth is the world does work like this. It did. That summer day in July, the woman I love twirling her engagement ring in the car, the setting sunlight projecting prisms on the roof, I shielded my eyes—not from pain—but from how brilliant the world was and how every shadow—in my brain—for the time being, simply disappeared.

∽

But I fear.

I shudder.

Wouldn't you?

Even now, when a headache comes, I brace myself for the worst. It's as if a hurricane approaches, and I have to board up all the windows and extricate all the furniture from the bottom level of the house for fear of flooding. This is the dread this pain brings. I think every headache is a hurricane.

Still, I never talk about it. I keep this pain a secret. To give voice to it is to acknowledge its existence. To acknowledge its existence is to dare it to come back, is to summon it into being.

Existence. Summon. Being.

Words for the supernatural. Words for the unreal.

Once a friend asked at a bar, "What was the worst pain you've ever felt?"

Too drunk to stop my mouth, I said, "A headache."

"Really?" He took an incredulous sip of his beer, shaking his head.

"Yep," I said.

"A tractor ran over my foot," he said. "You're lucky. Only thing you need is some aspirin."

I was not lucky. I could've told him the severity of the pain. I could've spoken about how I wanted to end it all. Could've said I wished one thousand tractors would run over my foot, flatten it into the texture of the blacktop. But I didn't want to burden him with my pain. Would he believe me anyway? Would he be able to conceptualize the enormity of what I felt? Would he believe a headache is capable of debilitating a person?

I don't want him to know. I don't want anyone to. I want the world to be blissfully ignorant of pain like this. There is so much pain out there already. Eating at us. Digging through us. Pain of the mind. Of the body. Of our culture. Our lives. Pain that erodes. Pain that dissembles. Pain that obliterates and erases.

No, he doesn't need to know. No one does.

Atlas, Don't Let Me Down

I was tired of myself. Tired of my ashy skin, my thinning hair, my lispy voice. Tired of looking in the mirror and seeing me, this obese, thirty-year-old Thai-American, a bad Buddhist, who worked at a university in upstate New York where snow weighed heavily on branches as did my thoughts. I saw only the physical in that mirror: my chins, my bulbous cheeks, the darkness around my eyes, my chapped and dried lips.

Tired. There was no other way to describe it. I was robbed of words, my mental acuity vanquished to some uncheck portion of my brain. TIRED was the billboard of my life. TIRED. T-I-R-E-D.

How I functioned those years, I do not know.

This exhaustion affected my work life, my relationship with students. During office hours, I was quick to get them out and on their way, quick to cut them off, not allowing them to speak freely about whatever it was that was on their minds; this should've been my red flag. I prided myself on the individual attention I gave students. But when you are deep in it, it's hard to see beyond the self.

The problem: I couldn't stand myself. I wanted a new identity, wanted to possess another's skin, experience the world with an entirely new vision. How I envied those movies where characters switched lives! How I wished it were a permanent Halloween and I'd slip into a mask and pretend Ira, the old Ira, disappeared!

This is the language of depression. At the time I didn't know it, only felt it, this drain, this sense of uselessness. To stave off these feelings I made wrong decisions. Though I was tired—ridiculously tired—I found the energy to want. I wanted everything. I wanted more pizza, noodles, fries. I wanted a car, a flat-screen TV, a pool table. This, I thought, would be the cross to my vampiric depression. This, I thought, would cure me.

And it did. For a moment. Soon, the world got heavy again. I hoisted it up on the flab of my shoulders, like the titan Atlas, felt its weight begin to buckle my knees.

‽

It was simple then. Our wants were our way of understanding the world. Our wants were predicated on who we envisioned ourselves to be. I wanted a fire truck because I wanted to be a fireman. I wanted a model of the space shuttle because I wanted to be an astronaut. These were logical steps a child made.

But there is more behind these wants, aren't there? I wanted to be a fireman because I wanted strength and courage in the face of danger. I wanted to be an astronaut because I wanted the ability to fly out of this atmosphere, to travel the cosmos.

To be young and fearless. To be young and imagine the impossible.

This isn't about youth. It's about wanting. It's about knowing what you want and why you want it.

When you suffer from depression, this issue of wanting isn't clear. Imagine you are bobbing for apples, something I did once when I was five. Imagine in that barrel filled to the brim with shockingly cold water are thirty or forty apples, and imagine all but one of those apples is rotten. Those apples are your wants. And here you are above this barrel of rotted wants, even though they glow in red luster, seductive in their gleam. You plunge your face into that barrel, and the apples move away from your chomping mouth, violently adrift in the wake of your face. And finally, after swallowing mouthfuls of water, your teeth pierce the taut skin of an apple and you emerge, water dripping off your nose and hair. But what of that apple clamped between your teeth? What of its bitterness? What of its acidic tang? Was it worth it? Is it worth another plunge for something sweeter?

☙

Why do therapists always ask how we are feeling? Bad, we say. What's bad? they say. I don't know. Bad. Clarify, they say. Bad is bad. Opposite of good. You know…I feel like shit. A simile, they say. Keep going with this. You feel like…a stalled heart… like someone gave me an instrument I have no clue how to play… like I'm completely naked…like a dream where I'm endlessly falling…like bobbing for bad apples…like a broken light bulb…like a downed tree still trying to sprout leaves…like the world is on my shoulders…like I want to drop it all.

☙

When I was five or six, my father and I threw darts at a world map on our living room wall. The map covered the entirety of the wall, and underneath it was trippy 70's style wallpaper, the design resembling laughing gold heads.

From the couch on the opposite wall, my father threw a dart. It landed in an ocean, like most of our throws. The world was covered in water.

I threw a dart and it stuck in eastern China.

"You will be China's next emperor," my father said in Thai.

"I like egg rolls," I said.

"All the egg rolls you can eat," he said and threw another dart, which stuck in Brazil. "You know what they say in Brazil?" he said.

I shrugged.

"Brazil things."

We continued to throw darts, continued to talk about the countries they landed on, continued to dream and imagine. Most of the time the dart landed somewhere neither of us knew, so we made up stories. "France is for fries." "Borneo is so boring."

Maps were easy places to dream, and my father was a dreamer. He came to America with lofty aspirations—owning a gas station, opening up a restaurant and spa. None of this happened, but it never deterred him. He kept dreaming. Kept wanting. No matter how unachievable, no matter how impossible. I envied this about my father: his ability to want.

And here we were. An immigrant father and his immigrant son. Wanting the world. With a map, you knew where you stood because everything was labeled, because there were roads that connected to other roads, borders outlined with thick lines, water a pale blue, mountains and hills in slight topographical curves.

It was easy for us to want.

I want South Korea.

I want Botswana.

I want New Zealand.

I want Portugal, Cuba, India.

I want, Father. All of it.

Take me there.

Let me breathe the air of a foreign land.

ↄ

The brain is not a map I understand. A southern friend has a phrase she often uses to describe difficult-to-grasp subjects: "Well, ain't that a hot mess." And the brain is. It is the hottest of messes. It is made up of billions and billions of neurons and cells. There are more pathways in the brain than there are roads on our Earth, yet the brain is the size of a small roasting chicken and resembles a deep-sea sponge.

This complex little muscle is the house of our every desire, our every mood. It tells us what we are in need of, or what we think we are in need of. It does not speak to us; we speak to it. We say, "Come on, Brain, think." We say, "Make sense out of this, Brain." We, at times of desperation, say, "Brain, why are you making me feel this way?" Actually, we rarely say that. Instead we say, "Why do I feel this way?" as if "this way" were separate from ourselves, as if the outside world contained the solution to this very inside situation.

What we forget is the brain is prone to fuck up. It happens a lot. And sometimes, most of the time, these fuck ups are not easy fixes. Scan it. Map it. Search for the misfiring problem. It's like locating a needle in one billion haystacks.

Recently, researchers have found the part of the brain where major depression dwells, Brodmann's area 25 (BA 25). This area of the brain controls sleep, anxiety, appetite, mood, memory formation and self-esteem. When mapping the brain of patients suffering from depression, scientists found BA 25 overly stimulated, like someone forgot to close the gate, as a researcher said, and because that gate remained open, it allowed for negative emotions to come in and stay and affect mood. This is the unwelcomed guest syndrome. We leave open the door, and suddenly, Depression walks in and begins to eat our dinner, sleep in our bed, watch our TV, and while he's doing that, he's telling us our food is too salty, our bed is too hard, and the TV is too staticy. He, in fact, is making snide remarks on every facet of our lives. The incredible thing is not that we are allowing the criticisms; it's that we begin to believe them.

❧

Depression says, "You want to buy that fifty-inch flat screen that costs more than your month's paycheck."

You say, "OK."

Depression says, "You want to eat another basket of fries even though you are already full."

You say, "OK."

Depression says, "You want that convertible with the outrageous monthly payment."

You say, "OK."

Depression says, "You should plan an outrageous trip to Hawaii even though you can't afford it."

You say, "OK."

OK, OK, OK.

OK is an easy response. After all, it's two letters.

ↄ

I watched a sitcom once where one of the main characters lusted after a carnie. The carnie was not rich, was not handsome. He was—in every sense of the word—average. (Well, not too average. He was a carnie after all.) This attraction to this average carnie perplexed a lot of the main character's friends. Why did she lust after this average carnie? Why must she be locked in a room like a werewolf on a full-moon night? Why must her phone be confiscated while the carnival was in town? What did this average carnie have that the hunky, chisel-chested male lead did not?

Answer: The carnie was literally brain damaged, and that damaged brain of his made him not want anything from this world. He just didn't give a shit, and the fact that he didn't give a shit was the biggest turn on ever.

My problem was I gave a shit. About a lot of things, so many things that I couldn't keep anything centered in my brain, so many things that it seemed to drain me of all my energy. I was no longer interacting with the outside world, but found myself dwelling inside my head, in my brain, this strange planet. I began to sink into the soft sponge of it.

ↄ

Buddha became Buddha because of want. He wanted to find a way to assuage suffering, and it was his own suffering he felt, the first pangs of it that made him pursue a solitary life. I imagine him, that boy prince, crumpled in a heap of despair after his first visit into the village, escaping the confines of the kingdom, despite how sheltered his parents kept him. I imagine what it might have felt like to set eyes on suffering—the old, the sick, the dying—and how that sense of helplessness set in, like a constricting snake. It was this pain that drove him away, that made him take his first steps towards becoming Buddha.

And so the boy prince sought the woods and lived years in meditation, failing at first to diffuse this hurt inside him. Did his meditative mantra begin with *I want, I want*? Did his chest and head ache from the weight of that hurt, that dark cloud, that depression? Did doubt ever creep into his mind? Did it feel—like it often felt for me—like he faced an insurmountable task?

Many years, many seasons, passed before Buddha discovered the solution to suffering: the brain, that mysterious muscle, which began to glow with higher wisdom, which resonated with a new mantra. *I am, I am.*

☙

I come from a Buddhist family who feel deeply. I have uncles in Thailand who lurk in the darkness, who go months without checking in. My mother was deeply depressed when she lived in the states, though she would never admit this. Her sisters, too, carry the sadness gene. But we never speak of this. We pretend nothing is wrong. We hide it.

But I'm beginning to think it goes beyond that. I'm beginning to think we never speak of our suffering because we don't know how to describe it.

And therein lies the problem. How can we describe something without detail? How can we describe vague feeling? We rest on loaded terms like bad, tired, sad. We begin to look for outside sources—our childhood, our mothers, our fathers, past relationships—anything to explain this pain we feel. We seek medication—Prozac, Celexa, Paxil. We look for logic in an illogical disease.

This logic is what our culture clings to.

A student a few years ago wrote an essay about depression and how depression suddenly manifested itself in her day to day life. Unbeknownst to her she had given depression the pronoun "she," and "she" was causing chaos. The narrator was no longer sleeping. She had sad thoughts. She didn't eat. Her peers picked up on the intrusion of the "she" and commented on how effective this device was. "She's like a bad friend," someone said. "One you can't get rid of. Like a shadow, you know?" Another student asked how "she" got there in the first place. "How can 'she' just be there? And can't you just make 'she' go away?"

Our culture has ingrained into us that depression is a failing of the human spirit, as suggested by this particular student when expressing that we can make depression disappear. Our culture also thinks depression is a response to a stimuli, and if we can locate that stimuli, then we can work on healing. It's a notion perpetuated in movies and shows. It's the fatal stereotype writers fall into. But why did Virginia Woolf walk into the river, pockets full of stones? Why did Plath stick her head in the oven? No matter what cause, these deaths are not normal effects.

I am not suggesting depression to be solely a neurological issue, that all blame should be put on the brain. Virginia Woolf suffered from self-doubt, Plath from the pains of her husband's infidelity. What I'm saying is the brain is a muscle, and because it is a muscle it can fail us like anything else biological.

༄

Fun Fact: What is the name of the vertebrae that holds up the brain? Atlas.

I am golfing with a friend when he says his brother wants nothing anymore. The course is backed up, so we're sitting in the golf cart chatting away. It's upstate New York, and the grey clouds are heavy from the west, which means cold rain.

"Is your brother depressed?"

"Nope," he says. "He seems happy."

"But not wanting?"

"He says he has a good job, a good wife, a couple of kids. There's nothing to want any more?"

"How about world peace?" I say.

"Are you a hippy?" my friend says.

I shake my head. Laugh. "What's living if you don't want anything?"

"That's what he says."

"Do you want anything?" I ask.

"Right now, I want to hit the golf ball. And after that, I want a beer and a hot dog. And maybe after that, I want some action with my girl." He looks up at the sky. "I don't want it to rain."

"Bigger," I say.

"Bigger what?"

"Bigger wants?"

"Listen," he says. "So, yeah, I want there to be no war. I want all dogs to have homes. I want people to not be so closed-minded. But I can't control the bigger. My brother, he's simple. He'll say he wants the Bills to win the Superbowl. That's as big and impossible as he'll get."

I nod.

"How about you?" he says.

"I don't know."

He laughs and in the distance there's the echo of thunder.

"I want to be a better person, I guess."

"You are a hippy," he says.

We say nothing until it's time to hit, and I think maybe it's not what we want, it's how bad we want it. I think of monks in Thailand with one set of robes, an alms bowl for food, and one pair of cheap sandals. I think about their simple meals, their day-to-day life. Their wants are simple. Their wants are necessities in life. I wonder if Buddha's way of combating suffering is to rid yourself of excessive wants, so that you can focus on what really matters. I wonder if ridding yourself of this excessiveness frees up the brain, lightens the weight of our thoughts.

It's my turn to hit. I line up toward my target, holding the club lightly in my hands. I know if I make solid contact I can make the ball curl toward the flag, stop it on the green. Right now, I want this to happen; it's all I want. And it does. The first drop of rain wets the earth.

వ

When I was in Naples, Italy, I fell in love with the sculpture of Atlas holding up the globe. I was twenty, and my study abroad class traveled all across Italia. Then, I smoked a pack a day and was in love with a girl in the class with the name of a shiny orange stone. I was also entering my first dark period in my life, when suddenly, it seemed I didn't want to do anything but smoke and eat and drink. For this reason, I went on this summer trip, to make myself leave the confines of my small apartment in southern Illinois, to make myself engage with the outside world.

On a quick daytrip excursion, we visited the National Archeological Museum of Naples. We were instructed to be careful in Naples, crime capital of Italy. We were told to keep together and try not to stand out, though I was Asian, and had not seen another Asian in Italy except for a group of elderly Japanese tourists following each other like ducklings. I stood out already—my big body, my yellow complexion, my English tongue—and this thought made me feel like I could not fit in wherever I was, not here, not anywhere. That was what I wanted. To fit in. To be loved. Though, at the time, I had not a clue of this.

I was getting tired. We all were. We walked about ten miles a day, our feet full of blisters. Though I liked my classmates, I only wanted to be with the girl I loved who had eyes for the chiseled Adonis on the trip. I was yearning for that small apartment again, yearning for time in my head, which wasn't healthy.

At the museum in Naples, we went from one thing to the next. I wasn't paying attention anymore. Etruscan pottery looked like Etruscan pottery. The marble statues of the gods were everywhere—Zeus, Aphrodite, Athena, Apollo. Their static eyes seemed to follow my every step. I was tired of the gods and their overbearing power. In most of the stories we were learning in class, they were bullies.

And there was Atlas. Naked and bearded Atlas, shouldering the heavens. It was a punishment, this weight-bearing. Zeus commanded Atlas to hold up the heavens for his role in the war against the Olympians. I circled the sculpture, took Atlas in.

I thought then about the burdens we carry. That each one of us suffers. That each of us bears some weight on our shoulders, and sometimes, we may not know what that weight is. A sadness entered me I had not felt before, one of pity, for myself, yes, but also for Atlas and his pained expression—his curled lips, his sad eyes—and I wept right then, wept silently into the sleeve of my polo I was instructed to wear because Italians wore polos. The girl I loved came up beside me and asked me what was wrong. I could not tell her because I did not know. I only felt it, and it sagged my shoulders, made me curl at the waist as if someone had punched me. "You want some air?" She took my hand and we walked outside.

"I hear this happens a lot," she said. "I cried last week and I didn't know why. It's culture shock." She rubbed my back, and I nodded. I knew this wasn't culture shock. This was a sadness deeper than displacement.

"Do you want anything?"

Naples was warm, and I knew it wasn't a good idea to stray from the class, but I did want something. I wanted it badly, more badly than the girl I loved.

"I want ice cream," I said.

"OK," she said. "Should we—"

I pulled her with me along the dusty streets of Naples, past ornate fountains, past Corinthian-columned museums, until we found a small gelato cart. I ordered two la fragola gelato with my fingers, and the girl I loved and I ate them under the Italian sun, the sweet tang sliding down my throat. I felt happy just then. I was not sure if this happiness was a fleeting sense of satisfaction. But I think I felt the happiness of a child, a child with ice cream, a child whose only concern was with the immediate. And the immediate was this: I was in Italy and with me was this girl I loved whose skin seemed to glow in the sun, who wore a long skirt that covered her ankles because Italian women wore skirts that covered the ankles, and who was here for the moment because she witnessed a boy cry over a statue in a museum and she cared.

"I want, like, another," I said. "It's the only thing I really want right now. You know what I mean?"

She didn't, I was certain, but nodded anyway, melted gelato dripping off her fingers the color of a luscious apple.

Meditation on Monsters

When I was six, I visited Thailand and made my cousin Ant draw me monsters. He was a far superior artist, and all he wanted to do was to please his American cousin. He sketched pages and pages of monsters, filling my notebook with Frankenstein and Dracula, werewolves and mummies.

After a few days of constant drawing, he said in Thai, "Would you like me to draw Buddha? I'm good at drawing Buddha."

I shook my head. Buddha didn't howl at the moon. Buddha didn't drink blood. Buddha was not constructed of decaying body parts. Buddha was boring.

"You know these things don't exist," he said. He was three years older, skinny like the bamboo stalks outside, had dimples so deep they could swallow fingers.

"But they do," I said. "In America, they are everywhere."

ຊ

I knew a woman once who was afraid of everything. How she hid from sight when the doorbell rang. How she never spoke a word to strangers and refused to meet eyes. How she did not venture out into the world, except to go to work. "There are too many monsters out there," she said. And so she raised her son in the same way. To fear the unknown. To be wary of anyone in America, because America was a place where bad things happened. America kidnapped children. America beat elderly men. America murdered unsuspecting women. This woman, despite her fear, watched the news daily with puckered lips and a shaking head. She relished the news, which fed her fear. When her son asked her why she surrounded herself with all the wrongs of the world, she said, "It's better to see. Better to know what hunts you."

๛

The first monster I met was Dave Colewell, aka Dak, aka Southside Terror. Dak was a few years older than me, and he had the habit of roaming the Chicago streets in his dirty jeans and jean jacket. He wasn't big, but beefy, hands like sledgehammers, face riddled with acne. He picked at his face, so there were large scabs and bloody raw spots on his cheeks and chin, like someone who had leprosy. Schoolyard rumors circulated about him: Dak threw third graders into car windows for fun; Dak mauled someone's face until it was minced meat; Dak set a cat on fire.

Of course I feared Dak. Of course seeing him coming down the street that afternoon as I was walking back from school put dread in my steps. The city block seemed infinite and dark and unnaturally silent. I kept my head down. Stared hard at the tufted grass poking out of the cracks of the sidewalk. I thought if I kept my head down, my shoulders hunched, I could disappear. I could be like the cars parked in driveways, the trimmed bushes, the mailboxes. I could be a thing. But I wasn't a thing because I breathed and my breath was loud, and my heart thumped fast, and I sweated despite the cool autumn day.

Dak's footsteps got louder and louder on the blacktop, the scrape of his gym shoes, the slight drag of his untied laces.

I told myself not to look up.

"Yo."

I kept walking.

"Yo, kid."

I turned my eyes toward Dak. I think I might have been tearing up.

"Yo, you know what time it is?"

Time for me to get my ass kicked. Time for me to be thrown into a car window, this car window, an Oldsmobile station wagon with wood siding. Time for me to be part of this growing legend of Dak, part of a story that started with, "Dude, once Dak took this Asian kid. . . . "

"Yo," Dak said.

I looked at my watch. I told him the time, my voice a hushed squeal.

"Thanks, kid." He kept walking.

Why tell this story if I wasn't going to be pummeled? Why bring you to the brink of danger and not deliver?

Because monsters, real monsters, aren't monsters all the time.

Because monsters, real monsters, are more complicated than we give them credit for. To show that monsters, real monsters, like Dak come from hard families. That they are beaten down by their fathers. That they live in small mobile homes with rusted out holes on the side covered in plastic. That they are stripped of all that is beautiful in the world.

That monsters, real monsters, sometimes just want to know the time.

☙

What do we really fear?

I've been thinking about this. I've trying to understand our—my—obsession with monsters. My childhood friend said watching a horror movie, reading a horror novel, allows us to forget the real world and our real problems. My childhood friend dropped out of high school, got kicked out of his house, became an alcoholic, and was a father at the age of sixteen.

For me, an immigrant's son, there was little difference between monsters and me. I was Frankenstein. I was a vampire. I was Freddy Krueger and Jason Voorhees. I was a howling werewolf. Strip these monsters of their monster monikers, and what are they?

Frankenstein: a child confused about his existence.

Vampires: a group of emo kids fretting about mortality.

Freddy and Jason: the inability to let go of the wrongs done to them in their lives.

Werewolves: the lack of control over uncontrollable anger.

Every monster, you see, is constructed of very human characteristics. The creation of a monster is bringing to the front the vulnerabilities and darknesses of being human.

℘

A friend of mine can't forgive himself for his past sins. He possesses red hair like a banshee, a voice that vibrates walls, the color black his everyday uniform. "I was a monster," he says.

"Looks don't count," I say.

"Ha ha," he says. "But seriously, I did really bad things."

"We all do."

"Not like this."

It's hard for me to think of my friend in any other way than who he is now—this soft-spoken intellectual with a penchant for horror novels. He's a gentle soul. He would stop his life to come to your aide.

I don't ask him what's he done. I don't want to know. I don't want to know because I fear what I might hear. I don't want to know because to give voice to our sin is to look it in the eye, is to give it shape and power over us.

"We're all monsters," I say.

We are. Jekyll and Hyde. To be human is to be capable of unmentionable things. To be human is to possess both good and evil.

℘

In southern Thailand, terrorist insurgent groups are beheading monks, burning temples, raping children. What really, I ask you, should we fear?

☙

My mother, when she lived in Chicago, never used the dryer. The rumble of one made her think of dead heads tumbling round and round, eyes bloodshot and popped open, canines bared. She said she imagined opening the dryer lid and heads flying out dizzily, bumping ears, foreheads, and noses against the walls like lottery balls. Instead, she hung our laundry outside, the warm Chicago breeze billowing the sheets, my T-shirts swaying like spastic ghosts.

☙

When I first traveled to Thailand at three, I noticed mini houses everywhere—in the yards of bigger homes, on busy streets in front of gas stations, at temples. Some of the houses were as intricate as the temples—the outer walls inlaid with jewels, gold shimmering in the Southeast Asian sun.

My aunt Jeeb had one on her property in Bangkok, and I imagined the house occupied by people as big as my Lego men, living secret lives no one knew about. The house stood in the front garden, surrounded by wild vines that laced themselves through the front fence, under a tree with leaves in the shape of half-inch canoes. Each morning, before the sun rose, my aunt and I lit incense and prayed in front of the house.

One morning, I asked her about the meaning of the houses.

"San Phra Phum," she said, *spirit homes*. My aunt was a schoolteacher and she spoke like one. She explained that spirit houses were part of a tradition from a time long ago, part of an animistic belief that predated Buddhism. I never knew something existed before Buddha. I was still under the impression that Buddha was like God, and that there was no world before he came into existence. The houses, she continued, were for the ghosts that lived on this land. We paid our respect to them every day, so those ghosts would protect us from wandering evil spirits or the occasional bad luck that might befall the property, like torrential rain that caused floods or the ill-willed thief.

"What do they look like?" I asked. "The spirits?"

She smiled. She looked like a younger version of my mother, but slighter, her hair beginning to gray at her temples. "Invisible," she said.

I remember peering into the house, through the windows, the front door. I squinted to focus. And perhaps it was the trick of the light or the whirling wisps of incense, but there was a shadow, I thought, that glided against a wall and disappeared out the miniature window.

ↄ

In a time of war, it is easy to label our adversary as "monster." It is to strip them of every virtuous quality. It is to strip them of complexity. Nietzsche said, "Whoever fights monsters should see to it that in the process he does not become a monster. And if you gaze long enough into an abyss, the abyss will gaze back at you."

ↄ

My mother and I huddled around the TV to watch Thai soap operas. Thai soap operas were typically thirteen episodes long, and during the summer months, when I did not have to go to elementary school, we halted our lives to exist only in the world of our small-screened television set. My mother watched these soaps because they kept her connected to her birthplace. It was the reason she read Thai novels and magazines, why she only purchased Thai ingredients at the Thai grocery store. I watched them because it was time with her, a woman who never kept still. I watched because sometimes I got to see a monster swallow a man's head in the cheapest and cheesiest way possible.

Thai soap operas were still soap operas. Filled with love and betrayal, melodrama and tears. Lot and lots of tears. The twist to many of these soaps? The monster on the loose. So, while mourning a broken heart, you had to escape the clutches of a mutated beast. The soap operas were formulaic—most soap operas are— but, on an intellectual level, the monster represented a fear of the unknown. Beginning episodes kept the monster a secret. The show of its tail. The darting dark shadow in the tropical jungle. But fear slowly subsided, because the narrative about lost love, about a grandmother dying from a weak heart, about a skinny boy being bullied at school, took over. Soon, we forgot the monster and focused on the humans, who—in many, many ways—posed a far greater threat than any fanged beast. Near the end, the monster would morph into a tragic hero. We'd learn that humans created it. Mistreated it. Had taken what it valued most: its child. So yes, we wished death on the humans, cheered the monster after every murder. It became the vehicle of our vengeance. It served the purpose of our anger. The monster became our will to act out against all that wronged us. My mother would utter, "good, good," when bad characters died. I'd clap my hands.

In the end, however, like most Thai soap operas, the monster died, and then I would huddle my head into my mother, sobbing, and she would soothe my back and tell me it was not real. It was all made up.

಼

What lurks in the night is not some other. It is not some myth-ological best. Not some furry animal. What lurks in the night is us.

಼

So it wasn't a surprise then that I constructed a spirit house made out of Legos. It was a hodge-podge of colors, made out of a hodge-podge of Lego sets, built in a hodge-podge of architectual styles. And I placed it out on the back steps of our suburban home, where my mother placed her shot glass of coffee for the spirits of the house. Now, the spirits had a place to sleep, a place to call home. Now, when the monsters came to hit our mailbox off the post, my father wouldn't have to rush out to chase them off. When they egged our station wagon, when they called us "chinks," when they slanted their eyes, when they whipped apples against the white siding of the house, the spirits in my Lego home would chase them away, rescue us from all the ugly in the world.

જ

When I left Thailand that year, my notebook was filled with drawings of monsters. My cousin, however, snuck one last drawing in. It was Buddha. He glowed. His elegant hands on his lap, his pursed lips, his slim torso. Ant drew him perfectly, even the wrinkles of Buddha's robe, even the tiny bubbles around Buddha's head, even his elegantly curved lips. I loved my cousin's drawing, but during the nineteen-hour plane ride back to the states, I unconsciously drew fangs on Buddha and stitches on his forehead and bolts on his neck. Oh, how I imagined Buddha howling at the moon, entering rooms in mist and shaking us awake, dwelling under the bed, waiting to pull us under.

ॐ

Acknowledgments

I am forever indebted to the editors and journals where these essays have appeared.

"The Animatronic Dog," *Under the Gum Tree*
"Atlas, Don't Let Me Down," *The Southeast Review*
"Dog without a Bark," *Tampa Review*
"Eat," *Colorado Review*
"Fattest, Ugliest, Weirdest" & "Noisy Neighbor," *Crab Orchard Review*
"Meditation on Monsters," *Zone 3*
"A Mediation on Pain," *River Teeth*
"My Heart. Open." *Kartika Review*
"Secret," *Phoebe*
"A Sequence of Thoughts Without Any Kind of Order," *Bending Genre Blog*
"Summer Days, 1983," *Prime Number*
"Thirteen Ways of Looking at Fat," *Bellingham Review*
"Twitch, Blink, Shiver," *Spectator and Spooks*
"The Uncovering," *Diagram*
"Yummy," *Fourth Genre*

Special thanks to Trenton Doyle Hancock and James Cohan, New York, for permission to reproduce the following 2010 works by Hancock:

Buff and Britches, acrylic and mixed media on paper, 15 x 11 1/4 in.
Faster, acrylic and mixed media on paper, 13 1/2 x 16 in.
Mr. Mouth, acrylic and mixed media on paper, 10 x 6 5/8 in.
Self-Portrait with Tongue, acrylic and mixed media on paper, 16 x 13 1/2 in.
Sometimes We Can't Have The Things We Want, acrylic and mixed media on paper, 16 x 13 1/2 in
The Doorstop, acrylic and mixed media on paper, 13 1/2 X 16 inches

Right now, my dog Daisy is watching me as my son is entranced by some television program where farm animals are singing the alphabet. He will watch intently and then go over to Daisy and put his eighteen-month-old hand on her and say, *woof woof.* I love these moments. I love them because my son is learning how to love, and these moments of love have come to him via a Shih Tzu. Daisy is ever patient. She loves this boy, and not just because she benefits from the scraps of food he often drops. She loves him because, for her, the world is about love. Her being is about love. And despite the occasional calamities of her existence—her tail will be pulled, my son will get carried away with his exuberance and pat a little too hard, her sleep will be disrupted by a toddler's tantrum—Daisy is ever tolerant. I want my son always to know this love. I want him to learn to love from all species of life in this world. There is no better teacher than a dog.

I owe so much to so many people.

To my friend, Katie Riegel, who brought the first two dogs into my life and subsequently healed a broken heart.

To Richard Mathews and all the folks at UTP for your care and attention and editing prowess, for caring so deeply about this book and believing that it's good enough to publish.

To my family and friends both in the states and across the ocean in Thailand, your kindness and support are the shiny reason for this book.

To my students at the University of South Florida, your energy and your ambition fuel me every day, constant reminders of the importance of the writer's life and the necessity of a life of the mind.

To my daughters, Kassidy and Kourey, your presence in my life is a light I'll follow forever.

To the artist Trenton Doyle Hancock, whose wonderful work appears in this book. Brother, you made my writing dig deep at the big body. It was an absolute honor to have worked with you on this project. Please, go acquaint yourself with Trenton's work: www.jamescohan.com/artists/trenton-doyle-hancock.

And to Dee. You have my heart. Keep it close. Always.

About the Artists

JACQUI LARSEN (cover) is a painter and mixed-media artist who has exhibited her work widely. Highlights include *Three-Mile Radius and Animal Brilliance*, painting/poetry collaborations, *Women Beyond Borders*, an internationally traveling exhibition based at the Santa Barbara Museum of Art; *Metaphorically Speaking*, BYU Museum of Art, Utah; and *Ancient Fragments in a New Light*, Woman-made Gallery, Chicago. She has taught at Northwest College in Houston, Houston Community College, and at Brigham Young University, where she co-directed a Study Abroad program to Spain. She has also served on the Board of Directors for Art Access Utah. Her work has appeared in many literary journals, including *Gettysburg Review, Rattle, Tampa Review, Ellipses*, and *Folio* as well as on the covers of three University of Tampa poetry collections.

TRENTON DOYLE HANCOCK (section II) was born in Oklahoma City and raised in Paris, Texas. He earned his BFA from Texas A&M University, Commerce, and his MFA from the Tyler School of Art at Temple University, Philadelphia. His work was featured in the 2000 and 2002 Whitney Biennial exhibitions, at the time, becoming one of the youngest artists in history to participate in this prestigious survey. In 2014, his exhibition *Skin & Bones: 20 Years of Drawing* originated at the Contemporary Arts Museum in Houston and traveled widely. His work has been the subject of one-person shows at the Contemporary Art Museum St. Louis; the Ringling Museum of Art, Sarasota; the University of South Florida Contemporary Art Museum, Tampa; the Savannah College of Art and Design, Savannah and Atlanta; and other galleries in the U.S. and abroad. His work is in the permanent collections of prestigious museums, including the Museum of Modern Art, New York; Whitney Museum of American Art; the Metropolitan Museum of Art, New York; San Francisco Museum of Modern Art; Dallas Museum of Art; Museum of Fine Arts, Houston; Museum Boijmans Van Beuningen, Rotterdam, The Netherlands; and many others.

About the Author

IRA SUKRUNGRUANG received the American Book Award for his previous collection of essays published by the University of Tampa Press, *Southside Buddhist*. He is the author of the memoir *Talk Thai: The Adventures of Buddhist Boy,* and a collection of short stories, *The Melting Season*. He is also coeditor of two anthologies on the topic of obesity: *What Are You Looking At? The First Fat Fiction Anthology* and *Scoot Over, Skinny: The Fat Nonfiction Anthology*. His first collection of poetry, *In Thailand It Is Night,* won the Anita Claire Scharf Award and was published by the University of Tampa Press in 2013. His work has appeared in many literary journals, including *Post Road, The Sun,* and *Creative Nonfiction*. He teaches in the MFA program at the University of South Florida. For more information about him, please visit: www.budhistboy.com.

About the Book

This book has been set in Adobe Garamond Pro types, developed from the sixteenth century roman types of Claude Garamond and the italics of Robert Granjon. Adobe Systems type designer Robert Slimbach visited the Plantin-Moretus Museum in Antwerp, Belgium, for research while working on the font. He later wrote, "The experience of studying near flawless proofs of Garamond's and Granjon's types was a revelation which led to a major overhaul of the working design." Slimbach's original digital fonts, released in 1989, have been further refined with digital options available in the newer Open Type format. The result is a versatile and highly readable serif face that preserves the grace and proportion of classical letterforms while projecting a timeless and contemporary clarity. The book was designed and typeset by Richard Mathews at the University of Tampa Press.